Puzzles for
Mindfulness

ARCTURUS

ARCTURUS

This edition published in 2018 by Arcturus Publishing Limited
26/27 Bickels Yard, 151–153 Bermondsey Street,
London SE1 3HA

ISBN: 978-1-78828-203-1
AD005911NT

Printed in the UK

CONTENTS

Introduction

Mindfulness is a choice. Our choice. To focus our attention on this moment, here and now.

It sounds simple, but it can be hard. Our mind wanders, and we are easily distracted. The past throws its shadows, the future is uncertain, and before we know it, our thoughts have led us away from here, from now.

Mindfulness admits as much, and then reminds us that at any point we can return ourselves to now.

Research has shown that the ability to live in the present enhances our sense of well-being. Focusing our attention enables us to be more creative, more efficient, and much less stressed.

"The present moment is filled with joy and happiness. If you are attentive, you will see it."

Thich Nhat Hanh

Puzzling for mindfulness

Puzzles are a great way of developing mindfulness. Give each puzzle your full attention, and troublesome thoughts will struggle to distract you. Enjoy concentrating on the puzzles, finding your way to the solution.

This collection contains a wide variety of puzzles. Some are of a type you may already know; others may be unfamiliar. Try them all. Getting to grips with a new task, trying one approach and then another as you reach for the solution, inevitably keeps you in the present.

The puzzles include all the information you need to complete them, so if the solution seems far away, take that opportunity to observe your own frustration. Part of mindfulness is about observing your emotions, and then choosing your response.

As the filmmaker David Lynch once said: "Keep your eye on the doughnut, not the hole."

"Always hold fast to the present. Every situation, indeed every moment, is of infinite value, for it is the representative of a whole eternity."

Goethe

Making the most of mindful puzzling

The point is, reality is not just about what happens; it is also about what we *think* happens. Mindfulness reminds us that we are in charge of our thoughts. It reminds us too that there is a solution.

Before beginning each exercise, a breathing exercise may help to bring a sense of calm.

Focus on your breathing. Feel your chest expand with each in breath, and fall with each out breath. Is your breathing fast or slow? Notice the pattern. For the next minute, give your breathing your attention.

When you are ready to turn to the puzzles, make sure you are comfortable. As you set about each one, try to breathe mindfully. And when you find the solution, embrace the moment.

That satisfaction will help you prepare for the puzzle on the next page, or the next task in your day. By improving concentration, mindfulness improves our memory and our understanding. It also undermines our self-doubt.

So make time for these puzzles, and make time for yourself. This moment belongs to you. Enjoy!

We hope you enjoy the puzzles in this book, and that they help you to achieve a mindful and relaxed state.

**"Yesterday I was clever,
so I wanted to change the world.
Today I am wise, so I am changing myself."**

Rumi

1   Maze

Start at the top and find a path to the middle of the maze.

"Each morning when I open my eyes I say to myself: I, not events, have the power to make me happy or unhappy today. I can choose which it shall be. Yesterday is dead, tomorrow hasn't arrived yet. I have just one day, and I'm going to be happy in it."

Groucho Marx

Wordsearch: Harvest Time

Can you find all of the listed words hidden in the grid below?
Words run horizontally, vertically or diagonally, in either a forward or
backward direction.

A	W	Y	Z	E	N	I	H	S	N	U	S	G
O	S	E	V	R	E	S	E	R	P	I	R	F
B	U	I	U	G	Q	H	P	H	L	E	N	L
O	E	M	B	N	A	Z	B	O	D	I	S	G
U	L	E	U	I	M	V	Q	I	R	T	T	R
S	D	H	T	L	H	V	C	M	A	C	C	J
T	N	P	M	I	U	E	U	O	X	E	M	Y
L	U	D	W	O	S	G	G	K	X	D	T	O
H	B	P	U	T	K	E	E	R	A	H	S	I
W	R	H	U	Q	G	T	O	P	A	O	E	Y
U	T	J	R	I	E	A	S	T	C	P	D	E
D	R	Y	I	N	G	B	O	C	A	S	E	K
D	I	E	K	O	R	L	G	D	L	M	I	S
R	Y	G	D	E	H	E	N	W	B	T	O	F
R	D	L	H	Z	D	S	X	T	B	F	P	T

BEET	HERBS	SHARE
BUNDLE	HOPS	SILO
CIDER	HUSK	SUNSHINE
CROPS	OATS	TOILING
DRYING	PRESERVES	TOMATOES
GRAPES	RYE	VEGETABLES

"Don't believe everything you think. Thoughts are just that—thoughts."

Allan Lokos

3   Arroword

Solve the clues, then enter each answer in the direction of the arrows, one letter per square. When completed, the letters in shaded squares can be rearranged to form another word.

Variety of citrus fruit		Made of clay	Bare		Of a female		On purpose	Armada
Unit of heredity					Brownie			
Stan ___, film partner of Oliver Hardy							Embrace	
				Frequent	Decorate with frosting			
Avian creature	Based on sound reasoning or evidence							
Idealists	Revolve		Deed		Feed			
								Beeps, as with a horn
Erstwhile					Fitting			
Courtyard		Canter					Word of surprise	
					Inflated pride			
Vegetables		Opening that permits escape or release						
					Affirmative word			

4 Sudoku

Place one of the numbers from 1 to 9 into every empty cell so that each row, each column and each 3x3 block contains all the numbers from 1 to 9.

		5				2	7	
7		3	5	1			4	
	1		7		2		8	
			3	5		4		9
1			8		9			3
2		9		6	7			
	4		9		3		1	
	9			4	6	5		7
	6	2				8		

"To think in terms of either pessimism or optimism oversimplifies the truth. The problem is to see reality as it is."

Thich Nhat Hanh

5   Codeword

Every letter in this puzzle has been replaced by a number, the number remaining the same for that letter wherever it occurs. Every letter of the alphabet has been used. Substitute numbers for letters to complete the codeword.

It may help to cross off the letters beneath the grid to keep a track of progress, and to use the reference box showing which numbers have been decoded. Three letters have already been entered into the grid, to help you on your way.

3	8	17	6	11	2	■	19	10	23	20	10	23	9	8
24	■	■	22	■	20	■	22	■	■	8	■	2	■	24
4	10	9	10	18	16	23	2	■	16	23	3	2	12	6
5	■	■	9	■	6	■	10	16	22	■	■	20	■	17
8	8	18	2	■	16	23	15	■	10	20	22	16	19	6
■	1	■	20	■	8	■	21	2	6	■	■	23	■	10
2	23	13	21	16	23	9	■	25	2	25	25	2	22	21
26	■	16	■	11	■	10	1	2	■	2	■	17	■	2
7	24	2	11	11	2	20	■	2	11	10	25	17	2	20
24	■	1	■	10	17	14	■	8	■	2	■	11	■	■
16	4	25	10	16	22	■	10	23	21	■	6	10	4	25 P
17	■	8	■	11	8	1	■	10	■	24	■	■	■	10 A
16	20	16	8	12	21	■	17	16	11	2	23	12	2	22 R
6	■	23	■	10	■	■	2	■	6	■	16	■	■	6
2	26	6	2	22	16	8	22	■	21	2	10	22	11	21

A B C D E F G H I J K L M

N O P Q R S T U V W X Y Z

1	2	3	4	5	6	7	8	9	10 A	11	12	13
14	15	16	17	18	19	20	21	22 R	23	24	25 P	26

6   Odd One Out

One of these islets is different from the others in some way. Which is the odd one out?

7   **Criss Cross: Fruits**

The words are provided, but can you fit them all into the grid?

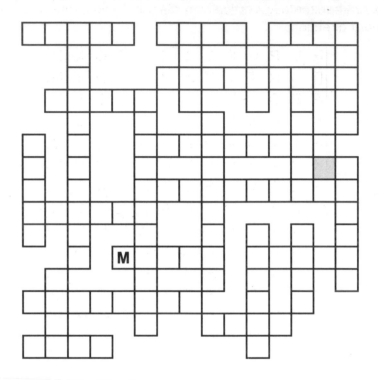

3 letters	5 letters	8 letters
FIG	APPLE	BILBERRY
	LEMON	TAMARIND
4 letters	MANGO	
AKEE	MELON	**9 letters**
DATE	OLIVE	CARAMBOLA
KIWI	PEACH	PERSIMMON
LIME		
PEAR	**6 letters**	**10 letters**
PLUM	LYCHEE	LOGANBERRY
UGLI	MEDLAR	
	ORANGE	**11 letters**
	POMELO	HUCKLEBERRY
		POMEGRANATE

Wordsearch: Calm Down

Can you find all of the listed words hidden in the grid below?
Words run horizontally, vertically or diagonally, in either a forward or
backward direction.

R	U	P	R	E	L	I	C	N	O	C	E	R
R	S	R	T	I	Y	X	B	M	A	H	E	N
A	E	O	H	E	I	M	T	X	H	D	F	E
A	K	P	Y	S	M	A	Y	F	U	H	S	S
S	T	I	O	A	U	P	A	C	T	S	T	S
K	B	T	M	S	L	H	E	D	Z	I	E	E
X	L	I	M	A	E	L	T	R	L	N	O	L
W	P	A	X	B	E	N	A	L	X	I	G	H
E	J	T	T	A	E	F	G	X	E	M	G	E
X	S	E	G	T	B	O	I	L	W	I	U	P
T	Q	U	E	E	C	J	T	H	P	D	A	D
Z	E	I	F	J	B	T	I	D	B	B	T	G
Y	U	D	J	E	E	S	M	U	G	V	Z	V
Q	W	G	X	S	D	T	S	E	Q	T	V	U
S	T	E	A	D	Y	L	L	E	U	Q	D	L

ABATE	MITIGATE	REPOSE
ALLAY	PROPITIATE	SETTLE
DEFUSE	QUELL	STEADY
DIMINISH	QUIETEN	STILL
HUSH	RECONCILE	SUBDUE
LESSEN	REDUCE	TEMPER

"Mindfulness is a way of befriending ourselves and our experience."

Jon Kabat-Zinn

9   **Maze**

Start at the top and find a path to the middle of the maze.

"The measure of the moral worth of a man is in his happiness. The better the man, the more happiness. Happiness is a synonym of well-being."

Bruce Lee

10   Pyragram

Every clue in this puzzle is an anagram leading to a single-word solution. Correctly solve the anagram on each level of the pyramid and another word will appear, reading down the central column.

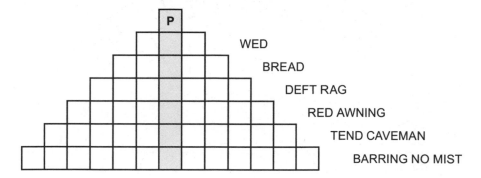

WED

BREAD

DEFT RAG

RED AWNING

TEND CAVEMAN

BARRING NO MIST

11   Word Wheel

How many words of three or more letters can you make from those in the wheel, without using plurals, abbreviations or proper nouns?

The central letter must appear once in every word and no letter in a section of the wheel may be used more than once.

There is at least one nine-letter word in the wheel.

Nine-letter word(s):

_____

Arroword

Solve the clues, then enter each answer in the direction of the arrows, one letter per square. When completed, the letters in shaded squares can be rearranged to form another word.

Very wealthy or powerful business-man	▼	Live-action film about a piglet	Panel forming the lower part of a wall	▼	Combat between two mounted knights	▼	Withered	Athletic facility
⌐					▼		Melody	▼
Crude oil		Afternoon meal	Grubby ▶			▼		
⌐		▼						
Type of chart	Interprets words		Docile horse used for ordinary riding	Belonging to that man		Caress gently		Free
⌐	▼		▼	For every ▶		▼		▼
Round objects used in games		Assistant ▶					Behind	
⌐				Small amount ▶		▼		
Russian monarch		Imitate	Repetition of some-thing to be learned	▼		Broadcast		Divisions of a day (abbr)
⌐		▼		Curse ▶		▼		▼
Follow orders	More con-temptibly narrow in outlook ▶							
⌐				Makes a mistake ▶				

13   Sudoku

Place one of the numbers from 1 to 9 into every empty cell so that each row, each column and each 3x3 block contains all the numbers from 1 to 9.

	3	9		6	4			
5	4					6		8
7	1			9		2		
	2		5					4
9		5	7		8	3		1
1					9		6	
		3		7			1	9
6		8					3	2
			4	8		5	7	

"Look at other people and ask yourself if you are really seeing them, or just your thoughts about them."

Jon Kabat-Zinn

14   Codeword

Every letter in this puzzle has been replaced by a number, the number remaining the same for that letter wherever it occurs. Every letter of the alphabet has been used. Substitute numbers for letters to complete the codeword.

It may help to cross off the letters beneath the grid to keep a track of progress, and to use the reference box showing which numbers have been decoded. Three letters have already been entered into the grid, to help you on your way.

22	18	14	7	12	1		16	20	13		9	17	22	24	16
19		19		16		12		17		17		10			23
11	22	12	18	17		24	22	4	18	22	6	13			26
14		18		19		2		12		18		20			18
20	14	12	2	22	14	24	16		24	16	17	20 **L**	22 **I**		10 **D**
		16		1			26		26						14
22	3	22	24		11	12	25	18	3	21	17	2	14		21
18		17		8		25		10		14		18			14
5	14	18	16	22	20	12	16	17	21		25	17	21		10
22			11		13			17		25					
24	20	14	14	11	13		15	26	22	3	3	20	14		10
22		21		14		16		11		16		14			25
3		12	22	21	24	23	22	11		12	10	10	20		14
20		24		14		22		14		22		4			20
14	19	14	18	10		24	16	21	22	18	4	14	18		16

A B C D E F G H I J K L M

N O P Q R S T U V W X Y Z

1	2	3	4	5	6	7	8	9	10 **D**	11	12	13
14	15	16	17	18	19	20 **L**	21	22 **I**	23	24	25	26

Wordsearch: Bright

Can you find all of the listed words hidden in the grid below?
Words run horizontally, vertically or diagonally, in either a forward or
backward direction.

```
G N I R E M M I H S G D I
E A T O L S E S Y L M L G
G N L N T E U Q E R L Q Z
N K G A E N F A L U L C M
I W D N N D M I M R I X E
W X I Y I I N I E G M P S
O X V J N N N E N R C S N
L X I G V A I I L H Y F E
G K V W T S L H E P B J T
L P J E T Z P E S G S H N
E U D A Z D R E A K Z E I
H S R A H F J R J C Z R R
J K D I U K I H A D X F P
W D Q L D S G N I Z A L B
A Q N J H R A E L C E H V
```

BLAZING	GLEAMING	RESPLENDENT
CHEERFUL	GLOWING	SHIMMERING
CLEAR	HARSH	SHINING
DAZZLING	ILLUMINATED	STARK
FIERY	INTENSE	SUNNY
GARISH	LURID	VIVID

"Open the window of your mind.
Allow the fresh air, new lights
and new truths to enter."

Amit Ray

16   Criss Cross: Summer

The words are provided, but can you fit them all into the grid?

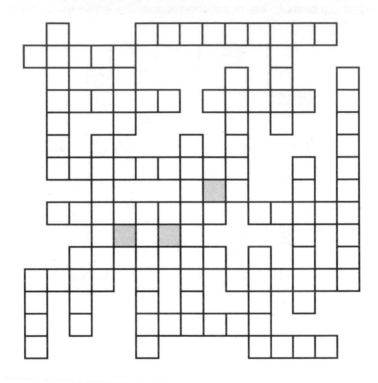

4 letters
JULY
JUNE
PLAY
SAND
TENT

5 letters
BEACH
LAGER
ROSES
WASPS
YACHT

6 letters
GARDEN
POLLEN
TENNIS
WARMTH

7 letters
DAY TRIP
HOLIDAY
MEADOWS
PARASOL
SEASIDE

8 letters
SWIMMING

9 letters
LAWNMOWER
PROMENADE
SEASHELLS

10 letters
DAISY CHAIN

Flower Power

Fit the listed words into the grid below, then rearrange the letters in the shaded squares to form another word related to the theme of this book.

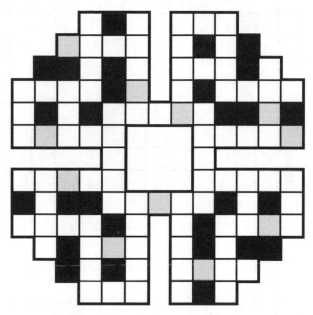

3 letters	4 letters		5 letters	
AGO	AREA	MAZE	ALIVE	LAPSE
ARC	BALE	MOSS	ARSON	RIGHT
BET	BLOW	ROAD	BASIS	SHIRT
EGG	CRAB	TEAM	BEAST	SWAMP
LIT	DEBT	THAN	BEING	TITHE
MET	FAIL	TORE	GLASS	TRESS
PIE				
SPA				

"You are the sky. Everything else is just the weather."

Pema Chodron

18   Maze

Start at the top and find a path to the middle of the maze.

 "The important thing is to realize that no matter what people's opinions may be, they're only just that—people's opinions. You have to believe in your heart what you know to be true about yourself. And let that be that."

Mary J. Blige

19   Sudoku

Place one of the numbers from 1 to 9 into every empty cell so that each row, each column and each 3x3 block contains all the numbers from 1 to 9.

1		4						6
		2		7	4		9	3
		7	2		8	5		
2	1			4	9			
	5		6		2		8	
			8	3			2	7
		5	9		1	6		
8	9		3	5		7		
3						9		1

"Everything that has a beginning has an ending. Make your peace with that and all will be well."

Jack Kornfield

20   Arroword

Solve the clues, then enter each answer in the direction of the arrows, one letter per square. When completed, the letters in shaded squares can be rearranged to form another word.

Blood feud		Platform		Gesture		At liberty / Improve in quality		Garland of flowers
								Wood nymph
Animal's line of descent / Henpeck				Blyton, author / Tidings				
Main meal of the day							Informal con-versation	
			Popular pub enter-tainment		Extremely cold			
Affirmative word		Basic unit of money in Malawi						
					Owned			
Book of maps		Belonging to me		Cleaning implement		Actor's portrayal of someone		Small green vegetables
Three-some	Army rank / Equip						Went in advance of others	
				Native of Warsaw, for example				
Very dark, black / 'S'-shaped moulding					Field suitable for grazing by livestock			
				Marries				

21   Wordsearch: Jewels and Trinkets

Can you find all of the listed words hidden in the grid below?
Words run horizontally, vertically or diagonally, in either a forward or
backward direction.

```
B K J K U T Q O R E A D S
R Q T Q E J A C R K Q D O
E T P K O G R C H Z A G A
T T C E H N A O L E P J F
E O R C A I E Y B A W L N
L R O H O R O C V N S N G
E Q W O L Y L J K V T P R
C U N K G T N S Q L N K Y
A E S E I I M N O O A Y F
R D D R A N C E H P D C G
B W I H O R T E P H N B E
P H C A I E M I C Q E O M
E I X E D T M T A H P I X
J H L S R E A A L R M U R
R R A C S W M E C H A R M
```

BEADS	CLASP	NECKLACE
BRACELET	CLIP	PEARLS
CAMEO	CROWN	PENDANT
CHAIN	DIADEM	TIARA
CHARM	ETERNITY RING	TORQUE
CHOKER	LOCKET	WATCH

"If you dance daily, you
shall expel any seed of
distress in thy soul."

Lailah Gifty Akita

22   Codeword

Every letter in this puzzle has been replaced by a number, the number remaining the same for that letter wherever it occurs. Every letter of the alphabet has been used. Substitute numbers for letters to complete the codeword.

It may help to cross off the letters beneath the grid to keep a track of progress, and to use the reference box showing which numbers have been decoded. Three letters have already been entered into the grid, to help you on your way.

11	22	7	13	22	8	1	17	2	■	7	■	23	■	14
10	■	1	■	23	■	22	■	6	23	26	2	1	■	5
11	22	23	21	9	1	23	8	2	■	1	■	14	■	1
17	■	1	■	4	■	■	23	2	19	2	5	23	■	10
2	16	17	23	22	26	15	4	8	■	2	■	15	■	12
12	■	1	■	2	■	■	6	24	5	■	21	■	■	1
■	21	6	4	20	22	2	11	17	■	10	2	1	11	17
11	■	■	26	■	23	■	1	■	9	■	12	■	■	2
17	6	14	1	25	■	8	10	23	1 (A)	17	15	4	8	■
23	■	2	■	6	19	1	■	■	23 (R)	■	8	■	■	2
15	■	2	■	6	■	7	6	6	12 (M)	2	23	1	4	8
21	1	23	1	12	2	5	■	5	■	1	■	■	■	23
18	■	1	■	15	■	2	3	3	2	21	17	15	19	2
2	4	8	15	4	2	■	23	■	11	■	2	■	■	11
4	■	2	■	8	■	21	6	4	11	15	26	2	23	11

A B C D E F G H I J K L M

N O P Q R S T U V W X Y Z

1 A	2	3	4	5	6	7	8	9	10	11	12 M	13
14	15	16	17	18	19	20	21	22	23 R	24	25	26

23 Jigsaw

Which four shapes (two black and two white) can be fitted together to form the graceful swan shown here? The pieces may be rotated, but not flipped over.

A

B

C

D

E

F

G

H

I

J

K

L

M

24 Criss Cross: Mindfulness

The words are provided, but can you fit them all into the grid?

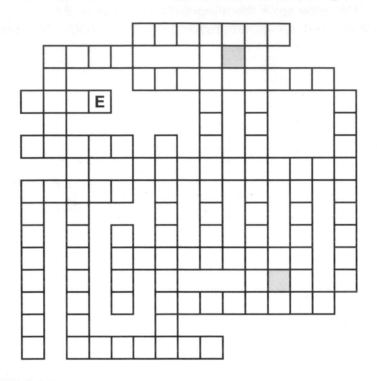

4 letters
CALM
CARE
SOUL

5 letters
FOCUS
PEACE
SPACE

7 letters
ESSENCE
INSIGHT
RESPECT

8 letters
FEELINGS
INFINITY

9 letters
AWAKENING
AWARENESS
OPENING UP

10 letters
ACCEPTANCE
MEDITATION
PERCEPTION

11 letters
PERSPECTIVE

13 letters
CONTEMPLA-TION

25   Pyragram

Every clue in this puzzle is an anagram leading to a single-word solution. Correctly solve the anagram on each level of the pyramid and another word will appear, reading down the central column.

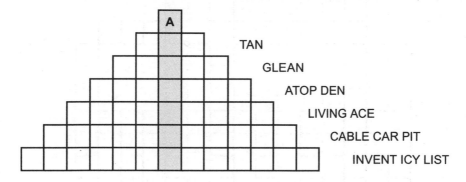

TAN

GLEAN

ATOP DEN

LIVING ACE

CABLE CAR PIT

INVENT ICY LIST

26   Word Ladder

Change one letter at a time (but not the position of any letter) to make a new word – and move from the word at the top of the ladder to the word at the bottom using the exact number of rungs provided.

27   Maze

Start at the top and find a path to the middle of the maze.

"I discovered that joy is not the negation of pain, but rather acknowledging the presence of pain and feeling happiness in spite of it."

Lupita Nyong'o

28　Wordsearch: Making Life Worthwhile

Can you find all of the underlined words from the poem "Making Life Worthwhile" by George Eliot hidden in the grid? Words run forward or backward, in either a horizontal, vertical, or diagonal direction.

U	S	P	E	G	A	T	I	R	E	H	H	E
E	G	N	I	N	E	K	C	I	H	T	L	E
E	K	O	S	T	T	N	E	E	D	I	G	A
O	C	A	O	T	A	L	M	K	H	E	B	G
L	L	A	M	D	M	L	E	W	T	R	N	T
H	I	B	R	A	V	E	H	F	I	I	C	H
T	M	F	E	G	V	T	E	G	N	I	A	G
I	H	L	E	G	R	S	H	E	N	U	I	U
A	G	C	Q	O	P	T	K	E	J	C	S	O
F	A	O	W	M	E	R	D	I	R	L	K	H
A	S	P	I	R	A	T	I	O	N	E	I	T
E	W	L	D	D	C	O	U	R	A	G	E	A
B	G	Y	L	D	N	I	K	H	H	D	S	Y
W	I	S	E	H	E	A	V	E	N	C	K	A
E	L	T	T	I	L	A	T	L	E	S	F	K

Get <u>there</u> from some <u>good</u>,

Some <u>little</u> <u>grace</u>; one <u>kindly</u> <u>thought</u>,

One <u>aspiration</u> yet <u>unfelt</u>,

One <u>bit</u> of <u>courage</u>,

For the <u>darkening</u> <u>sky</u>,

One <u>gleam</u> of <u>faith</u>,

To <u>brave</u> the <u>thickening</u> ills of <u>life</u>,

One <u>glimpse</u> of <u>brighter</u> <u>skies</u>,

To <u>make</u> this life <u>worthwhile</u>,

And <u>heaven</u> a sure <u>heritage</u>.

29   Arroword

Solve the clues, then enter each answer in the direction of the arrows, one letter per square. When completed, the letters in shaded squares can be rearranged to form another word.

Relating to plants	Time of life (3,3)	Having appendages on the feet	▼	Drag	▼	Prescribed selection of foods	▼	Light narrow boat
⌐	▼	▼						
Mr Reed who had a 'Perfect Day' ➤			Epoch		Bring out an official document			Bare
Excision, cut ➤			▼		▼		▼	
⌐		Applauded		Body of salt water ➤				
Evil	Restricts the number or amount of ➤	▼				Mentally or physically infirm with age ▼		
⌐			Mousse	Application ➤				
Metal device which rings	Kin group	Concurred ➤	▼					
⌐	▼			Behave	Baby's bed		Informal term for a father	
Ambit	Calm ➤	▼		▼	▼		▼	
⌐		Popular carbonated drink ➤						
Attention	Marked with spots ➤							

Sudoku

Place one of the numbers from 1 to 9 into every empty cell so that each row, each column and each 3x3 block contains all the numbers from 1 to 9.

	5	3	2					1
9					6	3		8
	4		9	5		6		
				1	2	7	8	3
		6				4		
7	2	8	5	3				
		7		8	9		1	
2		9	4					7
3					1	5	6	

"There is something wonderfully bold and liberating about saying yes to our entire imperfect and messy life."

Tara Brach

31   Codeword

Every letter in this puzzle has been replaced by a number, the number remaining the same for that letter wherever it occurs. Every letter of the alphabet has been used. Substitute numbers for letters to complete the codeword.

It may help to cross off the letters beneath the grid to keep a track of progress, and to use the reference box showing which numbers have been decoded. Three letters have already been entered into the grid, to help you on your way.

20		23		13	21	12	9	6	11	25	14	26	17	13
13	3	13	22	25		13			6		7		14	
11		22		12	9	15	24	14	22	9	4	4	13	24
25	14	25	17	13		22			12		17		10	
18		9		23		13	7	4	17	5	19	13	13	11
6		15	13	13	24		5		14			16		4
17	9	10		9			15		1		4	9	14	23
15		6		17	9	11	11	5	13	24		4		13
13	13	17	11		4		25			5		5	16	9
11		9			4		13		19	5	6	23		24
11	22	23	9	2	17	13	23	11		23		9		11
	12		11		14			5		26	5	25	22	12
22	5	15	11	13	8	6	13	15	22	13		14		13
	1		13		6			14		17	5	5	11	13
9	13	11	25 **T**	12 **H**	13 **E**	25	14	22	9	17		15		25

A B C D E F G H I J K L M
N O P Q R S T U V W X Y Z

1	2	3	4	5	6	7	8	9	10	11	12 **H**	13 **E**
14	15	16	17	18	19	20	21	22	23	24	25 **T**	26

Shadow Play

Which of the shadows is that of the prancing pony shown here?

Criss Cross: Pets

The words are provided, but can you fit them all into the grid?

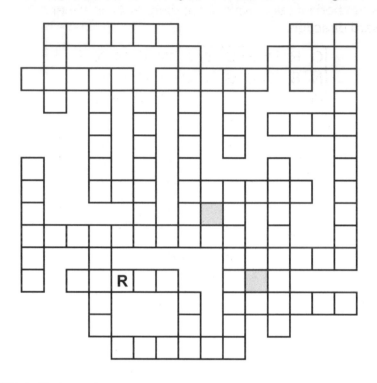

3 letters	MOUSE	8 letters
CAT	PUPPY	LOVE BIRD
DOG		TERRAPIN
RAT	**6 letters**	
	FERRET	**9 letters**
4 letters	GERBIL	GUINEA PIG
DUCK	KITTEN	
FROG	PARROT	**10 letters**
GOAT	PYTHON	BUDGERIGAR
PONY	RABBIT	
	SPIDER	**11 letters**
5 letters		STICK INSECT
GOOSE	**7 letters**	
HORSE	HAMSTER	

Wordsearch: Rainy Day

Can you find all of the listed words hidden in the grid below?
Words run horizontally, vertically or diagonally, in either a forward or
backward direction.

O	R	R	E	S	S	L	W	F	M	X	F	I
N	B	J	Z	G	J	D	R	H	R	S	V	N
O	I	R	L	R	U	D	X	W	O	B	S	S
I	H	Y	E	Y	E	L	R	N	T	W	E	O
T	G	O	A	T	O	W	E	I	S	E	H	D
A	U	N	O	M	A	L	O	D	Z	O	S	D
T	M	Z	I	D	H	E	L	H	P	Z	O	E
I	B	O	T	K	S	C	H	A	S	Z	L	N
P	O	N	E	Z	A	L	P	C	U	G	A	E
I	O	Y	K	R	L	O	N	U	D	Q	G	H
C	T	L	C	M	P	U	S	B	D	N	S	L
E	S	S	A	H	S	D	W	X	D	D	I	A
R	X	G	J	A	Y	S	I	Z	O	A	L	W
P	A	N	O	R	A	K	G	C	O	N	M	E
Y	J	N	V	X	Z	G	D	B	Z	H	L	P

ANORAK	GUMBOOTS	SOAKING
CLOUDS	HOOD	SODDEN
DAMP	JACKET	SPLASH
DELUGE	PRECIPITATION	SQUALL
DRIZZLE	PUDDLE	STORM
GALOSHES	SHOWER	WINDCHEATER

*"Take care of your body.
It's the only place you
have to live in."*

Jim Rohn

35   Maze

Start at the top and find a path to the middle of the maze.

"You need to learn how to select your thoughts just the way you select your clothes every day. This is a power you can cultivate."

Elizabeth Gilbert

36   Spot the Difference

In each of the pictures below, there is one detail different from the other pictures. Can you spot the one difference in every case?

37   Arroword

Solve the clues, then enter each answer in the direction of the arrows, one letter per square. When completed, the letters in shaded squares can be rearranged to form another word.

Indistinct shapeless form	▼	Disciple	Force by impact / Belief	►		▼	Young unmarried French-woman	Cut back
Molten rock	►	▼	▼		High mountain	►		▼
Stated one's views	►						Miraculous food	
►				Pre-dinner drink	Bird similar to an ostrich	►	▼	
Double-reed woodwind instrument	Itinerant Australian worker	►		▼				
News broadcast	Loan shark		Official emissary		A person in general	►		
►	▼		▼					Frame-work of a military unit
Oracle	►				Hollow, flexible structure resembling a bag	►		▼
Magni-ficent		Taunt	►				Do needle-work	
►					Hallucino-genic drug (inits)	►	▼	
Short		Farm implement used to break up soil	►					
►					Female sheep	►		

38   Sudoku

Place one of the numbers from 1 to 9 into every empty cell so that each row, each column and each 3x3 block contains all the numbers from 1 to 9.

	7		9		2		4	
3		1		6		7		2
2				1				9
9		4	2		3	1		5
	1		6		4		2	
8		2	5		1	6		4
6				4				8
1		3		5		4		7
	8		1		9		3	

"If we learn to open our hearts, anyone, including the people who drive us crazy, can be our teacher."

Pema Chodron

39   Codeword

Every letter in this puzzle has been replaced by a number, the number remaining the same for that letter wherever it occurs. Every letter of the alphabet has been used. Substitute numbers for letters to complete the codeword.

It may help to cross off the letters beneath the grid to keep a track of progress, and to use the reference box showing which numbers have been decoded. Three letters have already been entered into the grid, to help you on your way.

20	4	7	9	■	17	2	20	8	16	■	14	18	9	9
2	■	■	15	20	25	■	18	■	20	■	■	14	■	20
9	18	1	25	■	20	17	25	18	9	9	■	18	13	2
18	■	■	11	■	3	■	5	■	■	19	2	15	20	5
■	■	9	18	3	5	■	20	16	1	15	■	■	2	■
19	7	15	■	7	■	21	■	25	■	13	12	15	2	19
7	■	8	■	9	2	18	16	20	8	■	■	4	■	20
6	1	7	2	5	■	9	■	11	■	26	18	1	8	16
1	■	18	■	■	16	20	22	15	14	18	■	23	■	15
15	16	25	15	5	■	7	■	2	■	10	■	15	8	23
■	15	■	■	20	25	17	12	■	14 **B**	15	8	23	■	■
20	8	5	7	17	■	■	26	■	20 **A**	■	1	■	■	14
14	15	15	■	18	14	24	15	17	5 **T**	■	5	20	21	15
15	■	20	■	7	■	8	■	12	1	5	■	■	2
5	20	10	15	■	16	25	20	22	15	■	26	20	13	2

A B C D E F G H I J K L M

N O P Q R S T U V W X Y Z

1	2	3	4	5 **T**	6	7	8	9	10	11	12	13
14 **B**	15	16	17	18	19	20 **A**	21	22	23	24	25	26

Wordsearch: Aromatherapy

Can you find all of the listed words hidden in the grid below?
Words run horizontally, vertically or diagonally, in either a forward or
backward direction.

E	A	S	O	M	I	M	A	Y	Q	C	N	L
C	W	L	I	J	O	N	Q	U	I	L	E	R
F	Y	A	L	R	G	C	B	T	Q	O	E	D
L	X	P	O	F	J	N	R	F	V	G	R	J
I	Z	T	R	E	V	O	L	C	N	G	G	S
O	G	E	E	N	O	Y	I	X	F	R	B
R	G	M	N	E	S	O	G	N	A	E	E	B
G	T	N	L	R	B	S	R	E	K	G	T	M
V	F	L	A	P	Y	O	L	Y	U	E	N	C
W	A	E	S	M	S	Y	N	J	O	M	I	A
J	E	B	F	E	A	O	B	B	I	T	W	M
C	O	L	M	B	E	Q	Y	H	S	U	D	P
Q	C	A	E	P	J	A	S	M	I	N	E	H
H	R	R	Y	M	E	L	E	O	N	D	E	O
Y	Q	U	P	O	I	D	N	O	M	L	A	R

ALMOND	ELEMI	MYRRH
BAY LEAF	GINGER	NEROLI
CAMPHOR	JASMINE	NUTMEG
CITRONELLA	JONQUIL	PEONY
CLOVE	MANGO	ROSEMARY
CYPRESS	MIMOSA	WINTERGREEN

**"Go confidently in the
direction of your dreams!
Live the life you've imagined."**

Henry David Thoreau

41　　Criss Cross: Spring Bouquet

The words are provided, but can you fit them all into the grid?

4 letters
IRIS
LILY

5 letters
LILAC
PANSY
TULIP

6 letters
ALLIUM
SCILLA
VIOLET

7 letters
ANEMONE
COWSLIP
FREESIA

8 letters
BLUEBELL
CAMELLIA
DAFFODIL
FOXGLOVE
HYACINTH
PRIMROSE
SNOWDROP

9 letters
CELANDINE
HELLEBORE

Flower Power

Fit the listed words into the grid below, then rearrange the letters in the shaded squares to form another word related to the theme of this book.

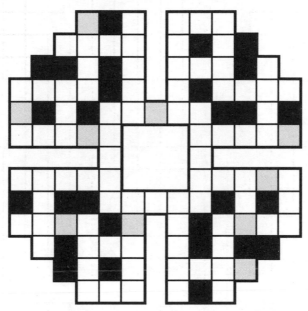

3 letters	**4 letters**		**5 letters**	
APE	EACH	MAID	ADEPT	LIMIT
ASS	FUSS	PATH	EXIST	PETTY
GOT	GIRL	PEST	FLASH	PLACE
HAT	GNAW	TART	FLIER	REPLY
LOT	GOLD	TOUR	FLOSS	TOTAL
MAN	LARK	TREE	HAPPY	WHEEL
POP				
TOW				

"Walk as if you are kissing the Earth with your feet."

Thich Nhat Hanh

43   **Maze**

Start at the top and find a path to the middle of the maze.

"There are two types of seeds in the mind: those that create anger, fear, frustration, jealousy, hatred and those that create love, compassion, equanimity and joy. Spirituality is germination and sprouting of the second group and transforming the first group."

Amit Ray

Odd One Out

One of these city sunset sky-line photographs is different from the others in some way. Which is the odd one out?

45   Arroword

Solve the clues, then enter each answer in the direction of the arrows, one letter per square. When completed, the letters in shaded squares can be rearranged to form another word.

Cross-breed	▼	Australian term for a young kangaroo	Consistent with fact or reality	▼	Catch sight of	▼	Added to	Bathing resort
⌐					▼		Cereal grass	▼
Indigestion		Add together	Appro-priate	▶			▼	
⌐		▼						
Throws away as refuse	Cinema attendant		Allegory	Girl's name		Cover with insulation to prevent heat loss		Deity
⌐	▼		▼	▼	One of the supports for a table	▶ ▼		▼
Onerous task		Distinctive quality	▶				Heavenly being	
⌐					Wander aimlessly in search of pleasure	▶ ▼		
Decapod crustacean		Beast of burden		Printing command to ignore a former deletion	▼	Egg cells		Enquire
⌐		▼		Roman cloak	▶	▼		▼
Domed recess	Parts of a garment which cover the arms	▶						
⌐				Babble	▶			

Wordsearch: Birds

Can you find all of the listed words hidden in the grid below?
Words run horizontally, vertically or diagonally, in either a forward or
backward direction.

```
L Y P H C I R T S O S D D
D R N O C L A F Y T O O S
T A Z Y F K J T M H O H T
A N F M H J B E E E E R R
T A A Q R G V L T R F A K
T C Y W E W O E L I G N I
L I E J S E W R D I K E C
E V R M T L Q T R K A A J
R K P M I Q V E F G X U W
D H S X O J G P V H U P Q
F W O R C D E D O O H I S
K T B U U Q L S Y K D G D
L O U B K I N G E I D E R
Q H O L T E N N I L S O B
G A O R A R E P J B X N D
```

BUDGERIGAR	KITE	QUAIL
CANARY	LINNET	ROOK
DOVE	OSPREY	SOOTY FALCON
EGRET	OSTRICH	STORK
HOODED CROW	PETREL	SWAN
KING EIDER	PIGEON	TATTLER

"Maybe that's what life is...
a wink of the eye and
winking stars."

Jack Kerouac

47   Codeword

Every letter in this puzzle has been replaced by a number, the number remaining the same for that letter wherever it occurs. Every letter of the alphabet has been used. Substitute numbers for letters to complete the codeword.

It may help to cross off the letters beneath the grid to keep a track of progress, and to use the reference box showing which numbers have been decoded. Three letters have already been entered into the grid, to help you on your way.

8	24	1	23	11	■	3	6	4	18	11	23	26	26	23
23	■	15	■	5	■	6	■	6	■	23	■	■	■	11
20	24	19	19	16	18	9	23	11	■	25 V	5 I	8 S	26	6
6	■	18	■	16	■	23	■	16	■	23	■	19	■	8
10	6	2	25	6	8	■	22	5	17	6	26	5	25	23
23	■	■	■	2	■	8	■	2	■	19	■	10	■	■
18	1	26	5	10	■	14	24	5	1	■	16	5	8	10
24	■	21	■	23	■	24	■	23	■	20	■	2	■	6
8	12	5	16	■	13	6	5	11	■	18	24	7	13	26
■	■	26	■	22	■	20	■	23	■	26	■	■	■	6
8	24	10	10	24	3	20	8	■	1	6	11	8	23	10
5	■	13	■	2	■	19	■	21	■	2	■	26	■	19
16	18	15	23	2	■	5	3	6	7	5	2	6	11	15
23	■	■	■	23	■	2	■	22	■	8	■	5	■	8
8	1	18	26	19	5	7	13	26	■	26	13	11	24	3

A B C D E F G H I J K L M
N O P Q R S T U V W X Y Z

1	2	3	4	5 I	6	7	8 S	9	10	11	12	13
14	15	16	17	18	19	20	21	22	23	24	25 V	26

48   Sudoku

Place one of the numbers from 1 to 9 into every empty cell so that each row, each column and each 3x3 block contains all the numbers from 1 to 9.

1		4	8				2	
	7		1					
		3		6	9	7		4
6		1			4	9		8
	3			9			5	
2		9	7			1		3
4		5	2	3		6		
					6		4	
	6				5	8		7

"Don't waste a minute not being happy. If one window closes, run to the next window, or break down a door."

Brooke Shields

49   Criss Cross: Gardening

The words are provided, but can you fit them all into the grid?

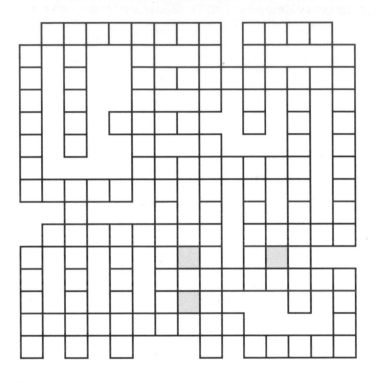

4 letters
CORM
LAWN
LIME
WASP

5 letters
ASPEN
LUPIN
MOWER
PLANE
STOCK

6 letters
EARWIG
GRAPES
TURNIP

7 letters
RAGWORT
WYCH ELM

8 letters
AUBRETIA
FEVERFEW
TARRAGON
WHITEFLY
WISTERIA

9 letters
SAXIFRAGE
TOADSTOOL

10 letters
CULTIVATOR
GYPSOPHILA
PROPAGATOR

11 letters
INCINERATOR

50   Matching Pairs

Can you identify six matching pairs of candles? Matching pairs are identical in every detail.

51   Maze

Start at the top and find a path to the middle of the maze.

"Most humans are never fully present
in the now, because unconsciously
they believe that the next moment
must be more important than this
one. But then you miss your whole
life, which is never not now."

Eckhart Tolle

52   Wordsearch: Loving Words

Can you find all of the listed words hidden in the grid below?
Words run horizontally, vertically or diagonally, in either a forward or
backward direction.

```
O K F N O I T C A R T T A
G D J O F P H D M B X R S
E N Q K N S Q C I X M Q S
T F I Q U D T T T P T P I
O J I V P P N R U R U F K
D A M X O N F E F E U C P
U E V Y P L E A S U R E U
U O S X V Z L R I S R Y K
Y Y D I K L E M R I E B F
E S G W R V G N A R D H Q
A A I S J E N P E U N O Q
R T D G N N A B I I E Q L
N S P T J U Q J F O T H R
C C L D W S L S R A G U S
O E S W J W J Z D J F E C
```

ANGEL	ECSTASY	PLEASURE
ATTRACTION	FONDNESS	SUGAR
CUPID	GENTLE	TENDER
CUTIE	IDOL	TRUE
DESIRE	KISS	VENUS
DOTE	LOVING	YEARN

"Grace, goodness, and gratitude are the heartbeat of a life well lived."

Lisa Cypers Kamen

53   Arroword

Solve the clues, then enter each answer in the direction of the arrows, one letter per square. When completed, the letters in shaded squares can be rearranged to form another word.

Lucky	▼	Silk fabric with a wavy pattern	▼	Ermine in its brown summer coat	Informal farewell remark (2-2)	▼	Jape	▼
►								
Cause to become widely known		Domesticated bovine animals		___ and don'ts, rules of etiquette	Baseball bat		Bony skeleton of the head	
►		▼		▼	▼		▼	
Praise, glorify	►					Out-standing musician		Sweet pepper
Garbage container	Chemically inactive		Add together (3,2)	►		▼		▼
►	▼		Egg of a louse	Island of Indonesia	►			
In addition		Bag made of hessian or plastic	▼	Amount owed	Common type of tree	►		
►		▼		▼			Hostel	
Charge	►				Can		▼	
►			Baked to a cinder	►				
And so forth (abbr)	Case for containing a set of articles	►			Yoko ___, widow of John Lennon	►		

54   Sudoku

Place one of the numbers from 1 to 9 into every empty cell so that each row, each column and each 3x3 block contains all the numbers from 1 to 9.

9					1	5	7	6
6		8				5		
3			8		6			1
			6	2		4	8	
	7		4		3		1	
	4	9		5	7			
1			7		4			9
		3				8		2
	6	5	2	9				4

"Being happy isn't having everything in your life be perfect. Maybe it's about stringing together all the little things."

Ann Brashares

55 Codeword

Every letter in this puzzle has been replaced by a number, the number remaining the same for that letter wherever it occurs. Every letter of the alphabet has been used. Substitute numbers for letters to complete the codeword.

It may help to cross off the letters beneath the grid to keep a track of progress, and to use the reference box showing which numbers have been decoded. Three letters have already been entered into the grid, to help you on your way.

19	8	20	21	5	4	6	21	15	■	7	10	23	8	6
4	■	23	■	18	■	4	■	20	■	8	■	8	■	5
22	20	24	10	18	■	20	1	1	8	16	8	18	■	4
5	■	10	■	10	■	14	■	26	■	7	■	20	■	1
22	8	2	20	7	17	8	22	■	25	4	22	21	8	18
■	■	4	■	15	■	■	3	■	22	■	■	■	■	1
7	5	5	21	■	18	8	21	10	24	8	22	20	7	8
4	■	4	■	7	■	26	■	1	■	18	■	11	■	6
22	8	6	4	22	2	8	1	9	8	■	5	11	4	6
24	■	■	20	■	18	■	■	■	23	■	21	■	■	■
4	1	24	8	1	7	■	24	22	8	20	26	10	1	2
21	■	20	■	12	■	8	■	5	■	18	■	9	■	10
8	■	21	20	4	1	18 **D**	22 **R**	15 **Y**	■	9	17	20	22	18
1	■	6	■	10	■	10	■	20	■	20	■	1	■	18
7	22	20	13	21	■	7	8	21	8	11	20	7	17	15

A B C D E F G H I J K L M

N O P Q R S T U V W X Y Z

1	2	3	4	5	6	7	8	9	10	11	12	13
14	15 **Y**	16	17	18 **D**	19	20	21	22 **R**	23	24	25	26

56   Jigsaw

Which four shapes (two black and two white) can be fitted together to form the leaf shown here? The pieces may be rotated, but not flipped over.

A

B

C

D

E

F

G

H

I

J

K

L

M

57   Criss Cross: Dances

The words are provided, but can you fit them all into the grid?

3 letters
BOP
JIG

4 letters
FRUG
REEL

5 letters
MAMBO
POLKA
RUMBA
SAMBA

SHAKE
TWIST

6 letters
BOLERO
BOOGIE
CHA-CHA
SHIMMY
VELETA

7 letters
TWO-STEP

8 letters
HABANERA
MERENGUE
MOONWALK

9 letters
ALLEMANDE
PASO DOBLE

10 letters
CHARLESTON
HOKEY-COKEY

58   Wordsearch: Make Me Laugh

Can you find all of the listed words hidden in the grid below?
Words run horizontally, vertically or diagonally, in either a forward or
backward direction.

```
I  M  J  I  K  C  I  T  S  P  A  L  S
U  B  A  C  I  L  O  R  F  P  L  S  S
C  J  K  N  J  F  F  F  W  Z  O  K  S
I  Z  O  E  D  A  R  A  H  C  A  O  H
G  Y  S  U  U  D  L  P  R  N  I  S  F
A  T  N  P  D  A  C  P  C  I  V  X
G  N  F  R  T  R  V  A  S  R  E  Q  E
S  I  T  C  O  M  N  A  E  G  I  S  R
T  A  B  D  X  T  T  B  J  O  N  E  P
H  D  Y  F  O  I  B  X  I  E  P  U  U
B  W  D  M  R  I  Q  Y  S  A  W  G  N
G  M  I  E  G  R  Y  N  C  J  O  K  E
A  M  Z  Y  H  O  O  T  E  Q  C  X  B
E  R  Y  R  E  N  O  O  F  F  U  B  L
P  X  I  J  F  Y  K  Q  Q  V  W  G  W
```

BUFFOONERY	GIBBERISH	PARODY
CAPER	IRONY	PUN
CHARADE	JEST	SATIRE
FARCE	JOKE	SITCOM
FROLIC	NONSENSE	SLAPSTICK
GAGS	PANTOMIME	SPOOF

"Not how long, but how well you have lived is the main thing."

Seneca

59   Maze

Start at the top and find a path to the middle of the maze.

"'May the Force be with you' is charming but it's not important. What's important is that you become the Force—for yourself and perhaps for other people."

Harrison Ford

60   Pyragram

Every clue in this puzzle is an anagram leading to a single-word solution. Correctly solve the anagram on each level of the pyramid and another word will appear, reading down the central column.

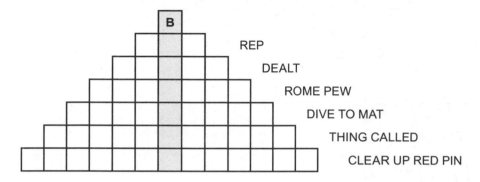

REP

DEALT

ROME PEW

DIVE TO MAT

THING CALLED

CLEAR UP RED PIN

61   Word Wheel

How many words of three or more letters can you make from those in the wheel, without using plurals, abbreviations or proper nouns?

The central letter must appear once in every word and no letter in a section of the wheel may be used more than once.

There is at least one nine-letter word in the wheel.

Nine-letter word(s):

_____

62   Arroword

Solve the clues, then enter each answer in the direction of the arrows, one letter per square. When completed, the letters in shaded squares can be rearranged to form another word.

Second letter of the Greek alphabet		Consign-ment		Of the highest quality		Christmas flower		Occasion for excessive eating or drinking
Yielding a profit								
Faucet				Greases		Primitive plant forms		City in western Germany
Rectory	Substance for staining a fabric		Small areas of land sur-rounded by water					
Angle that resembles the hind limb of a canine							Deliver-ance	
Part of a necklace		Love intensely	Look at intently					
				Adoles-cent				
Device used for exact timing	Bill in a restaurant		Cherry stone	Existed, lived		Attempt		Adult female bird
Elaborate song for a solo voice					Perennial herb with bitter-tasting leaves			
Makes a wager					Japanese currency unit			

63   Sudoku

Place one of the numbers from 1 to 9 into every empty cell so that each row, each column and each 3x3 block contains all the numbers from 1 to 9.

	6	7	1			2		
9						5	1	7
	5		3	4				
3			4	7			6	5
	1		6		8		9	
4	8			3	5			2
				9	2		5	
1	3	8						9
		2			3	6	4	

"A few simple tips for life: feet on the ground, head to the skies, heart open...quiet mind."

Rasheed Ogunlaru

64   Codeword

Every letter in this puzzle has been replaced by a number, the number remaining the same for that letter wherever it occurs. Every letter of the alphabet has been used. Substitute numbers for letters to complete the codeword.

It may help to cross off the letters beneath the grid to keep a track of progress, and to use the reference box showing which numbers have been decoded. Three letters have already been entered into the grid, to help you on your way.

7	19	2	20	24		2	19	3	20	17	1	19	9	20
19		6		6		17		16		8				6
2	24	8	19	9	19	20	17	23		8	17	3	19	8
6		20		7		24		15		12		18		7
8	15	16	6	1	3		6	2	15	2	1	19	14	16
20				19		7		24		20		19		
17	9	11	19	8		15	21	6	16		19	2	17	23
9		19		3		18		9		6		19		12
13	8	17	2		21	9	15	20		23	6	8	15	22
		13		10		1		3		23				22
21	17	9	21	6	4	15	12		5	12	6	8	8	16
6		19		9		6		6		3		19		24
8	6	7	17	17		7	19	3	2 P	19 E	8 R	6	7	15
26				19		19		24		8		25		1
6	3	3	12	8	19	7	1	16		3	17	19	25	19

A B C D E F G H I J K L M

N O P Q R S T U V W X Y Z

1	2 P	3	4	5	6	7	8 R	9	10	11	12	13
14	15	16	17	18	19 E	20	21	22	23	24	25	26

65   Wordsearch: Creatures

Can you find all of the listed words hidden in the grid below?
Words run horizontally, vertically or diagonally, in either a forward or backward direction.

```
R P H L C N A D J F R O M
U H D A P O H Y E N A I O
S U M A T O P O P P I H L
T E L B C E P K X N C D E
L A L C E O N I C J R W U
X M O H Y E A T K D U P G
O S S T O V I T W L Y B U
I J R I S Q X E I O V Z V
S N A I L O Z N C N S E D
P U I G D T E R R E F L X
N F I I U K U E K K L T G
R O N V P A K C O C A E P
A G S J K S R H E I F E R
O E E Z N A P M I H C B I
T S A U Q K D C F C H K L
```

BEETLE	DINGO	KITTEN
CAMEL	FERRET	MOLE
CHICKEN	HEIFER	PEACOCK
CHIMPANZEE	HIPPO-	SHEEP
COATI	POTAMUS	SNAIL
COYPU	HYENA	STOAT
	JAGUAR	

"Life's tragedy is that we get old too soon, and wise too late."

Benjamin Franklin

66   Criss Cross: Mountain Ranges

The words are provided, but can you fit them all into the grid?

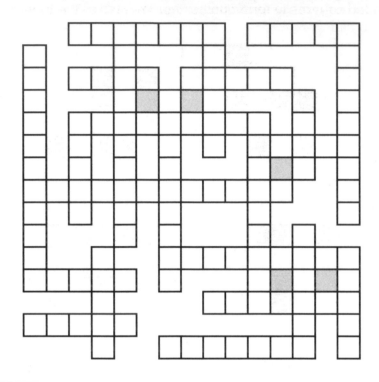

4 letters
JURA
KRAG

5 letters
AMARO
DAVIS
GYDAN
HARAZ
LEWIS
SAYAN
SHEEP
URALS

6 letters
PURITY
SEMIEN

7 letters
BISHOPS
CHERSKY
PREMIER

9 letters
GUADALUPE
HINDU KUSH
NEWCASTLE

STRANDZHA
SWARTBERG

10 letters
SERRA GERAL

11 letters
DRAKENSBERG

12 letters
SIERRA NEVADA

Flower Power

Fit the listed words into the grid below, then rearrange the letters in the shaded squares to form another word related to the theme of this book.

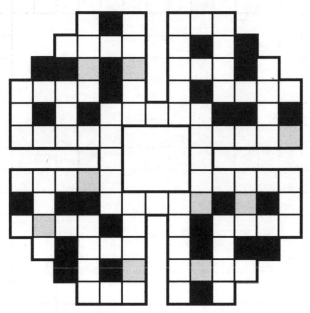

3 letters	4 letters		5 letters	
CUT	AWAY	MOVE	ATLAS	EXPEL
INN	BAKE	TENT	CLING	GLOSS
LIE	BAWL	TOAD	DITTO	LADLE
MUD	BEAK	TRAP	DRAMA	RANGE
PEA	DOOR	WAIT	ELVES	ROOST
PET	LEAD	ZONE	EXERT	TEXAS
RYE				
VAT				

"Life is a dance. Mindfulness is witnessing that dance."

Amit Ray

68   Maze

Start at the top and find a path to the middle of the maze.

"Perhaps ultimately, spiritual simply
means experiencing wholeness and
interconnectedness directly, a seeing that
individuality and the totality are interwoven, that
nothing is separate or extraneous. If you
see in this way, then everything becomes
spiritual in its deepest sense. Doing science
is spiritual. So is washing the dishes."

Jon Kabat-Zinn

In Place

Place the listed words horizontally into the grid, so that when read from top left to bottom right, the letters in the shaded squares spell out a word linked to the theme of this book. Some letters are already in place.

ANEMONE

CANDLES

DEVOTED

GIRAFFE

HABITAT

JOURNAL

TACTFUL

		B				
				T		
		C				
				N		

"The earlier you learn that you should focus on what you have, and not obsess about what you don't have, the happier you will be."

Amy Poehler

70 Arroword

Solve the clues, then enter each answer in the direction of the arrows, one letter per square. When completed, the letters in shaded squares can be rearranged to form another word.

Declare formally ▼	▼	'___ Lang Syne' Scottish song ▼	▼	Land measure ▼	▼	One third of 27 / Arched ▼	▼	Drenched with water
►		▼				▼		Bright and pleasant
Customary way / Belonging to us ►				Hard fruits / Calf meat ►				▼
Ingenious ►				▼			Light and insub-stantial	
►			Isolate		Delivery vehicle ►		▼	
Elderly		Cotton fabric with a shiny finish ►	▼					
►					Free from liquid ►			
Defama-tory writing		Conflict		Mr Garfunkel, singer-songwriter ▼		Charge		Hindu discipline
Country, capital Lima	Coquette / Large deer	▼				▼	Put on	▼
►	▼			Disorderly outburst or tumult (2-2) ►			▼	
Noble-woman / Scottish island ►					Cut part of a tree trunk ►			
►				Arm bone ►				

71   Wordsearch: Grow and Grow

Can you find all of the listed words hidden in the grid below?
Words run horizontally, vertically or diagonally, in either a forward or
backward direction.

E	O	X	Q	V	H	A	T	C	W	L	N	A
B	S	O	A	Z	J	N	U	P	Q	G	O	K
F	B	I	Q	W	D	E	E	P	E	N	U	X
L	S	P	R	O	L	I	F	E	R	A	T	E
A	V	W	Q	A	F	I	T	I	C	H	T	U
R	O	W	E	I	I	N	E	S	I	A	R	Y
E	N	V	L	L	U	C	P	C	L	I	M	B
O	T	M	X	O	L	R	K	L	M	N	P	X
U	A	A	M	Q	X	E	N	L	U	N	U	B
T	O	P	N	S	N	A	P	E	A	M	O	A
K	A	L	F	I	W	S	Z	C	D	P	P	L
C	H	O	J	F	M	E	C	G	O	I	E	L
B	E	P	L	B	N	R	Q	R	P	T	W	O
B	Z	C	F	B	U	S	E	M	O	O	B	O
S	X	H	U	E	K	I	I	G	B	U	N	N

ACCRUE	DEEPEN	PROLIFERATE
ARISE	FLARE OUT	RAISE
BALLOON	GERMINATE	SWELL
BLOAT	INCREASE	THICKEN
BOOM	MOUNT	WAX
CLIMB	PLUMP	WIDEN

"Life can only be understood backwards, but it must be lived forwards."

Soren Kierkegaard

Codeword

Every letter in this puzzle has been replaced by a number, the number remaining the same for that letter wherever it occurs. Every letter of the alphabet has been used. Substitute numbers for letters to complete the codeword.

It may help to cross off the letters beneath the grid to keep a track of progress, and to use the reference box showing which numbers have been decoded. Three letters have already been entered into the grid, to help you on your way.

19	5	17	21	14		22	12	24	5	14	16	12	12	3
11		7		17		17		5 H		17				16
2	13	24	17	16	4	17	1	17 E		8	17	14	2	11
8		16		26		10		22 M		17		17		13
24	16	11	26	17	21		17	8	12	24	17	16	2	4
23			16		21		17		11		25			
11	24	12	22	8		18	6	21	15		20	18	11	1
13		16		17		7		26		1		16		11
1	2	6	8		5	18	6	17		17	22	17	16	15
		11		23		16		8		4				21
11	22	13	2	12	24	2	4		6	17	22	2	13	2
14		9		13		11		19		22		13		6
14	21	11	15	8		13	11	2	21	23	16	18	8	5
21			11		4		24		17		16		24	
17	22	14	24	2	13	17	8	8		16	17	17	1	8

A B C D E F G H I J K L M
N O P Q R S T U V W X Y Z

1	2	3	4	5 H	6	7	8	9	10	11	12	13
14	15	16	17 E	18	19	20	21	22 M	23	24	25	26

73   **Sudoku**

Place one of the numbers from 1 to 9 into every empty cell so that each row, each column and each 3x3 block contains all the numbers from 1 to 9.

	6		9	5			4	7
2	7				3	1		
		4			2			
5	2		7				9	3
		6		9		8		
1	9				4		2	6
			5			7		
		5	8				3	4
7	8			6	1		5	

"Make the right decision
even when nobody's looking,
especially when nobody's looking,
and you will always turn out okay."

Oprah Winfrey

Criss Cross: Knitting

The words are provided, but can you fit them all into the grid?

4 letters	6 letters	8 letters
PURL	CAST ON	CARDIGAN
WOOL	DOUBLE	KNITTING
	MOHAIR	STOCKING
5 letters	POCKET	
BALLS		**9 letters**
GAUGE	**7 letters**	WAISTCOAT
HANKS	BLANKET	
HOBBY	LOOPING	**10 letters**
NYLON	MACHINE	TURTLENECK
SHAWL	TENSION	
SOCKS		
TWIST		
YARNS		

75   Pyragram

Every clue in this puzzle is an anagram leading to a single-word solution. Correctly solve the anagram on each level of the pyramid and another word will appear, reading down the central column.

MUG

BELLA

PERU LED

DIRTY ROOM

PLANET COMET

NOT BE GRATEFUL

76   Word Ladder

Change one letter at a time (but not the position of any letter) to make a new word – and move from the word at the top of the ladder to the word at the bottom using the exact number of rungs provided.

Maze

Start at the top and find a path to the middle of the maze.

"The most fundamental aggression to ourselves, the most fundamental harm we can do to ourselves, is to remain ignorant by not having the courage and the respect to look at ourselves honestly and gently."

Pema Chodron

Wordsearch: Happy the Man

Can you find all of the underlined words from the poem "Happy the Man" by John Dryden hidden in the grid? Words run forward or backward, in either a horizontal, vertical, or diagonal direction.

```
T S R O W O R D N N E M H
Y P E N H V M S E G E O E
E N O L A I A E V T U N S
T A Y S N Y B D A R N I F
O G Y E S J N F E G E A N
W E R U C E S N H W O R M
N I H T I W S J O Y S H B
Y P P A H S H S E L G H W
E M G E H E S A E N U O E
V F A I R P N W T D R O H
A Y N F L E S T I R K Y F
H E A L I V E D O L E A C
B Y G D E Y A M N T S A P
K R E W O P O R E R L T Y
F O R P E T I P S L A S O
```

Happy the man, and happy he alone,

He who can call today his own:

He who secure within, can say,

Tomorrow do thy worst, for I have lived today.

Be fair or foul or rain or shine

The joys I have possessed, in spite of fate, are mine.

Not Heaven itself upon the past has power,

But what has been, has been, and I have had my hour.

Arroword

Solve the clues, then enter each answer in the direction of the arrows, one letter per square. When completed, the letters in shaded squares can be rearranged to form another word.

Displayed	▼	Fruit resembling a small peach	Decoy, lure	▼	Coating of gold	Biblical character	▼	Irritation
Home ground ►		▼	▼			▼		Heavy book
Gemstone ►					Do something ►		▼	
Court order ►					17th letter of the Greek alphabet ►			
⚑				Forward movement	Golf club with a relatively narrow metal head		Acquire	
Interlace yarn in a series of connected loops	Brief stop		Flexible joint ►	▼	▼		▼	
Authority ►	▼					Proportion		Audibly
⚑			Large artery ►			▼		▼
Chapeau		Add up	Chemical carrying genetic information (inits) ►				Marry	
Cook slowly in liquid ►		▼			A couple ►		▼	
⚑			Au revoir ►					
Sign of the zodiac	Plaything ►				Curious ►			

80   **Sudoku**

Place one of the numbers from 1 to 9 into every empty cell so that each row, each column and each 3x3 block contains all the numbers from 1 to 9.

4	5			7	8		3	
7			4			6		
1		2	5				4	
	4	8		2				1
		9	1		6	2		
3				9		5	6	
	3				1	7		6
		5			2			8
	1		6	8			9	5

"When we get too caught up in the busyness of the world, we lose connection with one another—and ourselves."

Jack Kornfield

81   Codeword

Every letter in this puzzle has been replaced by a number, the number remaining the same for that letter wherever it occurs. Every letter of the alphabet has been used. Substitute numbers for letters to complete the codeword.

It may help to cross off the letters beneath the grid to keep a track of progress, and to use the reference box showing which numbers have been decoded. Three letters have already been entered into the grid, to help you on your way.

26	10	20	6	15	2		23	10	15	8	9	26	13	4
10		7		10			17			15		5		25
9	21	9	10	26	17	4	9	4		17	25	20	22	9
9		10		5		15		19		2		2		19
23	19	20	13	9	20	24		9	21	13	17	2	26	13
		22		4		13		9				9		
14	5	9	20	13		5	15	23	9	16	24	19	19	6
20				10			14			10				9
4	24	12	25	20	10	17	2	9		9	21	17	4	13
		19				1		10		3		2		
4	9	20	4	17	1	9		10	15	24	13	17	2	9
13		18		2		20		15		9		13		1
20	19	17	9	2		4	5 H	10	17	2	11	17	2	22
17		2		9			20 A			26		20		9
10	9	22	20	10	1	9	1 D		26	6	26	19	9	1

A B C D E F G H I J K L M

N O P Q R S T U V W X Y Z

1 D	2	3	4	5 H	6	7	8	9	10	11	12	13
14	15	16	17	18	19	20 A	21	22	23	24	25	26

Reflections

Which of the designs below is an exact horizontal (left to right) mirror image of the design to the right?

I

2

3

4

5

6

7

8

83   Criss Cross: A Walk in the Woods

The words are provided, but can you fit them all into the grid?

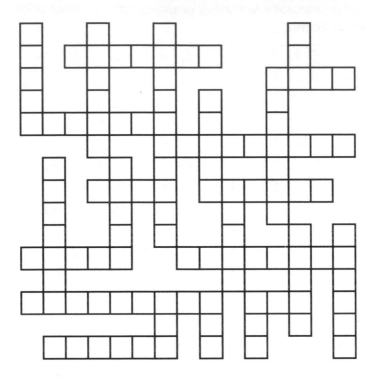

3 letters
ELM
FIR
IVY
OAK
OWL

4 letters
CROW
DEER

5 letters
BEECH
FENCE

HOLLY
MAPLE
TRUNK
TWIGS

6 letters
BEETLE
CANOPY
LEAVES
STREAM

7 letters
CREEPER
FOLIAGE

HEMLOCK
NETTLES

8 letters
PINE CONE

9 letters
BRIDLEWAY
CELANDINE

10 letters
BLACKBERRY

84 Wordsearch: Admirable Adjectives

Can you find all of the listed words hidden in the grid below?
Words run horizontally, vertically or diagonally, in either a forward or
backward direction.

```
T N E L L E C X E Q C F T
S P L E N D I D V H I A N
C T B X F M H D A V G H E
O M A E Q T O R R H P O C
M Q S G F N M D B D T N I
P A N A G I G E E N A E F
E T E T N E B L E S S S I
T T P G R V R I K H T T N
E R S V E U D I I K O L G
N A I S F E S N N O U O A
T C D L B P I T W G N V M
N T N O N N B A Y O D E X
V I I Y G Q M F W O I L M
J V J A W T F E A D N Y L
N E U L H B T E Y H G Q L
```

ASTOUNDING
ATTRACTIVE
BRAVE
CHARMING
COMPETENT
EXCELLENT

GOOD
HONEST
INDISPEN-
    SABLE
LOVELY
LOYAL
MAGNIFICENT

MODEST
OBEDIENT
SHINING
SPLENDID
STAGGERING
TRUSTY

"Life isn't about finding
yourself. Life is about
creating yourself."

George Bernard Shaw

85 Maze

Start at the top and find a path to the middle of the maze.

"We use mindfulness to observe the way we cling to pleasant experiences and push away unpleasant ones."

Sharon Salzberg

86   Shadow Play

Which of the shadows is that of the plane
shown here?

A

B

C

D

E

F

G

87　Arroword

Solve the clues, then enter each answer in the direction of the arrows, one letter per square. When completed, the letters in shaded squares can be rearranged to form another word.

Collection of ancient Scandinavian poetry	Depicted	Eat greedily		Bill ___, of Microsoft fame	Footwear	Musical pace		Opera by Verdi
				Agitate ▶				
Heaved ▶								Forty winks
Biblical first woman			Arabian sultanate ▶					
						Beard found on a bract of grass		
Ballroom dance in double time (2-4)	Single-celled organism		Shuts	Long-eared creature, similar to a rabbit				
					Cleansing agent	Equivalent		Lock of hair
Cause to wither	Dormant ▶							
					Loud utterance of emotion		Cereal crop	
Contributor	Safe ▶							
				Beams ▶				
Adept	Fashions ▶							

Sudoku

Place one of the numbers from 1 to 9 into every empty cell so that each row, each column and each 3x3 block contains all the numbers from 1 to 9.

	5		3		2			9
6	4		9	5				
3			4				1	8
		9		3	1	6		
5		6				7		1
		8	5	6		3		
1	8				5			2
				8	3		5	6
2			1		7		4	

"If you can do what you do best and be happy, you are further along in life than most people."

Leonardo Dicaprio

Codeword

Every letter in this puzzle has been replaced by a number, the number remaining the same for that letter wherever it occurs. Every letter of the alphabet has been used. Substitute numbers for letters to complete the codeword.

It may help to cross off the letters beneath the grid to keep a track of progress, and to use the reference box showing which numbers have been decoded. Three letters have already been entered into the grid, to help you on your way.

16	4	13	24	8	21	3	5		6	25	4	13	24	2
	13		8		4		10		25		3			9
3	25	12	9	4	13		14	3	8	12	16	17	5	17
	12		8		4		25		22		26			2
5		23	4	20	11	4	3	19		10	4	17	4	3
18		25			4		7	2	18	20		25		5
26	2	12	2	10	20	12		4		12	8	10	25	17
8		9		4		4		3		16		9		21
3 **L**	8	3	4	21		13		4	21	26	8	5	1	5
4 **A**		5		13	5	17	24		5			4		10
13 **R**	8	15	14	5		26	2	2	15	3	25	12		24
4			25		2		8		8		13		4	
24	5	4	24	2	11	5	3		3	8	9	8	15	2
5			17		5		5		3		4		22	
17	11	4	20	5	15		24	13	4	8	10	5	5	17

A B C D E F G H I J K L M

N O P Q R S T U V W X Y Z

1	2	3 **L**	4 **A**	5	6	7	8	9	10	11	12	13 **R**
14	15	16	17	18	19	20	21	22	23	24	25	26

90   Wordsearch: Clouds

Can you find all of the listed words hidden in the grid below? Words run horizontally, vertically or diagonally, in either a forward or backward direction.

```
L H K Y D C I R R U S N M
I G N I W O L L I B T C G
V J E T S T R E A M O Y V
N N O N S V F K B C R C L
A T O F O U F I Q M M L W
C W N L S I T V B O Z O I
E I N H I U T A I N E N S
M R H T T A E C M R U I P
D E U P X O T L E M L C Y
E D B L A C K S I V A S U
V N B J C R F A E P N M C
P U R B R L G N T R H O H
N H A K G D U O I I A W C
P T I A M R A G R I V M E
C O N T R A I L S O X R I
```

ANVIL	CYCLONIC	RAIN
BILLOWING	JET STREAM	SNOW
BLACK	MAMMATUS	STORM
CIRRUS	MARE'S TAIL	THUNDER
CONTRAILS	OROGRAPHIC	VIRGA
CONVECTION	PILEUS	WISPY

"Only those who dare to fail greatly can ever achieve greatly."

Robert F. Kennedy

91   Criss Cross: In the Greenhouse

The words are provided, but can you fit them all into the grid?

4 letters	SIEVE	7 letters
POTS	STAKE	PEPPERS
SOIL	WEEDS	SHADING

5 letters	6 letters	8 letters
BENCH	ORCHID	CUCUMBER
BOXES	PLANTS	PARAFFIN
HERBS	RIDDLE	SUNLIGHT
LABEL	SEEDER	
MULCH	STANDS	11 letters
SCOOP	TROWEL	WATERING CAN
SEEDS	WARMTH	
SHELF		

92   Flower Power

Fit the listed words into the grid below (one letter is already in place), then rearrange the letters in the shaded squares to form another word related to the theme of this book.

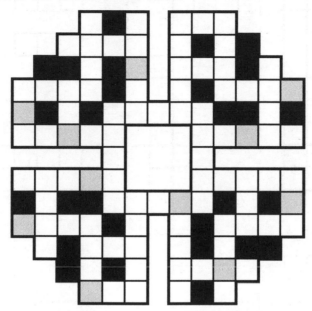

3 letters	4 letters		5 letters	
ASK	BACK	LINE	AMEND	OCTET
BOA	BOND	MOAT	DEFER	SABLE
EAT	DOZE	PAGE	FLUKE	TALON
HUM	EARL	TRUE	GAUZY	WIDEN
LAG	HOOT	WANT	MIAMI	WRING
OVA	LEAF	WREN	NOISY	ZEBRA
ROT				
TIP				

"Normal is nothing more than a cycle on a washing machine."

Whoopi Goldberg

93   Maze

Start at the top and find a path to the middle of the maze.

"While you'll feel compelled
to charge forward it's often
a gentle step back that will
reveal to you where you are
and what you truly seek."

Rasheed Ogunlaru

94   Jigsaw

Which four shapes (two black and two white) can
be fitted together to form the starfish shown here?
The pieces may be rotated, but not flipped over.

95   **Arroword**

Solve the clues, then enter each answer in the direction of the arrows, one letter per square. When completed, the letters in shaded squares can be rearranged to form another word.

Engage in espionage	▼	Resist separation	▼	Grooved surface of a pneumatic tyre	Contended	▼	State of the USA, capital Columbus	Animal doctor
Social outcast ▶		▼			▼		Country, capital San Juan (6,4)	▼
⚑				Fully developed ▶			▼	
Park in central London	Frequently visited place ▶							
⚑				Ebbed		Small insectivorous bird		Electrical resistance unit
In one's sleeping place	Repast		Fashion reminiscent of the past ▶	▼		▼		▼
George ___, English poet and novelist ▶	▼							
Floor covering		Contest of speed	Basic knitting stitch		Selleck, actor in 'Magnum PI' ▶			
⚑		▼	▼			Mental capacity		Novel
Praise or glorify ▶					Be victorious ▶	▼		▼
Area where animals graze	Cleft ▶							
⚑					Drag behind ▶			

Wordsearch: Cat Breeds

Can you find all of the listed words hidden in the grid below?
Words run horizontally, vertically or diagonally, in either a forward or
backward direction.

```
S O K O K E N O U W A X Y
P B E T T I A E S N Q T E
H Y B O L T I R N F H A S
Y B B A T O R W B A H R E
N M M A G E E O I A X O N
X O E N C D B J I E T K I
S T A S P E I E R S L N K
N O D L I T S K E G N A N
M A N X L A R N G E X G O
Y E I S D I M L B X V Q T
A P E S K A M E A I L V D
B A J L A D L R S G J D D
M E E J O U N K U E N M N
O S H D N T N W Y B R E J
B H F G E R M A N R E X B
```

ASIAN	MANX	SOKOKE
BENGAL	NEBELUNG	SOMALI
BOMBAY	PIXIE-BOB	SPHYNX
BURMILLA	SELKIRK REX	TABBY
GERMAN REX	SIAMESE	THAI
KORAT	SIBERIAN	TONKINESE

"Life is not a problem
to be solved, but a reality
to be experienced."

Soren Kierkegaard

Every letter in this puzzle has been replaced by a number, the number remaining the same for that letter wherever it occurs. Every letter of the alphabet has been used. Substitute numbers for letters to complete the codeword.

It may help to cross off the letters beneath the grid to keep a track of progress, and to use the reference box showing which numbers have been decoded. Three letters have already been entered into the grid, to help you on your way.

26	6	19	25 L	5 O	18 T		19		23	21	16	19	4	22
5		25		23	5	24	6	15		19		23		
24	5	9	5	17	15		7		6		21		21	
19		21		3		2	6	24	21	25	21	18	15	
25		24		13	6	24	18		19			24		6
	15	5	7	19		5		9		22	5	19	25	19
10				4	19	12	18	5	5	24		24		2
11	3	9	12	19		3		17		21	24	6	10	18
9		6		24	6	19	12	21	24	7				15
25	21	7	23	18		25		4		23	11	2	22	
21		21			14		2	6	4	18		19		3
4	5	24	8	11	6	2	18		12			20		6
	1		11		21		19		19	20	21	6	25	17
	6		21		12	6	24	6	14			2		19
11	24	21	18	6	17		22		25	6	24	18	21	25

A B C D E F G H I J K L M

N O P Q R S T U V W X Y Z

1	2	3	4	5 O	6	7	8	9	10	11	12	13
14	15	16	17	18 T	19	20	21	22	23	24	25 L	26

98   Sudoku

Place one of the numbers from 1 to 9 into every empty cell so that each row, each column and each 3x3 block contains all the numbers from 1 to 9.

5				7		3	1	
	8	1		9	4	2		
6	9	7	3					
4				6	5			
2	6						8	3
			8	2				4
					1	4	9	7
		3	9	8		5	6	
	7	2		5				8

"No matter what happens in life, be good to people. Being good to people is a wonderful legacy to leave behind."

Taylor Swift

99   Criss Cross: Spring

The words are provided, but can you fit them all into the grid?

3 letters	GREEN	SHOWERS
MAY	GUSTY	VERDANT
	MARCH	
4 letters	NESTS	**8 letters**
BUDS		BLUEBELL
EGGS	**6 letters**	CLEANING
LENT	CROCUS	
LILY	SHOOTS	**9 letters**
	TULIPS	MIGRATION
5 letters		
APRIL	**7 letters**	**11 letters**
BUNNY	BLOSSOM	PUSSY WILLOW
FEVER	RAINBOW	
FRESH		

100   Odd One Out

One of these ice creams is different from the others in some way.
Which is the odd one out?

101   Maze

Start at the top and find a path to the middle of the maze.

"It had long since come to my attention that people of accomplishment rarely sat back and let things happen to them. They went out and happened to things."

Leonardo Da Vinci

Wordsearch: Just Perfect

Can you find all of the listed words hidden in the grid below?
Words run horizontally, vertically or diagonally, in either a forward or
backward direction.

E	L	B	A	C	C	E	P	M	I	D	J	R
T	H	O	R	O	U	G	H	Y	E	N	E	I
E	A	T	G	G	Y	Y	F	H	O	M	R	M
P	J	S	C	S	I	D	S	M	A	E	U	M
P	R	S	E	N	M	I	N	T	O	U	P	A
R	O	E	V	Z	N	Z	C	R	V	D	G	C
E	Q	L	X	I	J	H	E	E	X	A	E	U
C	E	T	F	E	L	U	B	P	V	V	A	L
I	S	O	G	E	R	S	K	X	T	I	J	A
S	H	P	S	Y	A	I	E	E	C	T	W	T
E	E	S	U	E	I	N	T	A	A	R	F	E
B	E	D	P	D	M	L	J	N	X	N	M	T
L	R	D	E	C	N	E	I	R	E	P	X	E
U	L	A	R	G	L	S	I	S	V	D	E	T
I	L	E	B	W	M	S	T	A	E	N	A	G

ENTIRE	IMMACULATE	PURE
EXACT	IMPECCABLE	SHEER
EXPERIENCED	MATCHLESS	SINLESS
EXPERT	MINT	SPOTLESS
FINISHED	MODEL	SUPERB
IDEAL	PRECISE	THOROUGH

"I stand only with truth,
and my conscience is
my only leader."

Suzy Kassem

103   Arroword

Solve the clues, then enter each answer in the direction of the arrows, one letter per square. When completed, the letters in shaded squares can be rearranged to form another word.

Procession of people on horseback ▼	▼	Bowl-shaped vessel	▼	Engraving in relief	Collection of facts	▼	Long thick piece of wood used in building	▼
◄								
Warning device tripped by smoke (4,5)		Hasty		Unit of electric current	Deceiver		Helicopter propeller	
◄		▼		▼	▼		▼	
Girl's name ►					Bites off very small pieces	▼		Elegant, imposing ▼
Anti-tobacco organisation (inits)	Cramp		Gasps for breath ►					
◄	▼		For what reason?	Public violence ►				
Receptacle used to clean clothes or linen		Daze	▼	Examine	Woman's garment ►			
◄		▼		▼			Ailing	
Eye infection ►					Be in a horizontal position ►		▼	
◄			Aroma ►					
Flightless Australian bird	Negative word ►				Artful ►			

Sudoku

Place one of the numbers from 1 to 9 into every empty cell so that each row, each column and each 3x3 block contains all the numbers from 1 to 9.

		9			8		1	5
					5	3		
1	3		2	7			6	
6	5				3		2	9
		4		2		6		
8	2		1				5	7
	7			6	9		4	1
		1	7					
3	8		4			7		

"When you become the image of your own imagination, it's the most powerful thing you could ever do."

Rupaul

105   Codeword

Every letter in this puzzle has been replaced by a number, the number remaining the same for that letter wherever it occurs. Every letter of the alphabet has been used. Substitute numbers for letters to complete the codeword.

It may help to cross off the letters beneath the grid to keep a track of progress, and to use the reference box showing which numbers have been decoded. Three letters have already been entered into the grid, to help you on your way.

6	22	8	20	21	4	11	21	17		8	26	5	11	9
22		20		19		5		22		21		4		20
8	1	22	23	20		9	11	23	9	20	19	22	16	23
7		2		14		22		17		23		23		8
20	12	20	21	7	22	16	23		4	20	15	20	4	20
4			16		4		20		20		11		11	
22			10		16	24	20	8	20		10		17	
11	21	5	10 **M**	20	23		9		23	20	3	1	20	6
	16		11 **A**		22	9	22	16	7		22			4
	10		23 **N**		23		20		4		8			20
19	11	3	9	16	18		4	1	13	7	1	10	22	21
20		11		15		21		13		11		11		17
11	3	3	4	20	1	20	23	9		8	20	23	23	11
15		20		4		9		4		7		22		18
20	18	4	20	7		20	25	16	23	20	4	11	7	20

A B C D E F G H I J K L M
N O P Q R S T U V W X Y Z

1	2	3	4	5	6	7	8	9	10 **M**	11 **A**	12	13
14	15	16	17	18	19	20	21	22	23 **N**	24	25	26

106   Pyragram

Every clue in this puzzle is an anagram leading to a single-word solution. Correctly solve the anagram on each level of the pyramid and another word will appear, reading down the central column.

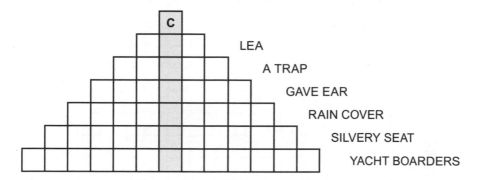

LEA

A TRAP

GAVE EAR

RAIN COVER

SILVERY SEAT

YACHT BOARDERS

107   Word Wheel

How many words of three or more letters can you make from those in the wheel, without using plurals, abbreviations or proper nouns?

The central letter must appear once in every word and no letter in a section of the wheel may be used more than once

There is at least one nine-letter word in the wheel.

Nine-letter word(s):

_____

108   Criss Cross: Gemstones

The words are provided, but can you fit them all into the grid?

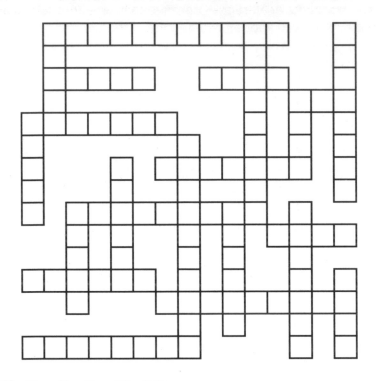

3 letters
JET

4 letters
JADE
ONYX
OPAL
RUBY

5 letters
AGATE
AMBER
PEARL
TOPAZ

6 letters
GARNET
QUARTZ
SPHENE

7 letters
KUNZITE
OLIVINE
PERIDOT

8 letters
AMETHYST
SAPPHIRE

9 letters
CORNELIAN
TSAVOLITE
TURQUOISE

10 letters
BLOODSTONE

11 letters
ALEXANDRITE

109   Wordsearch: Exciting Words

Can you find all of the listed words hidden in the grid below?
Words run horizontally, vertically or diagonally, in either a forward or
backward direction.

B	E	I	S	J	S	R	S	D	L	Y	K	U
W	R	R	E	T	A	T	I	G	A	A	N	P
E	D	U	I	S	X	S	L	J	O	W	N	C
S	N	U	N	F	T	E	J	I	L	S	C	L
A	E	R	I	U	P	T	I	N	C	I	T	E
E	A	T	R	M	E	I	G	N	I	T	E	H
T	V	B	I	L	A	L	D	J	H	T	F	Y
P	R	O	E	T	A	T	I	C	S	U	S	S
I	W	P	M	M	I	O	M	I	L	D	Y	T
B	J	I	U	O	Q	L	O	T	V	C	M	E
Q	K	D	N	K	C	P	L	N	Q	D	O	R
W	D	O	A	D	R	D	D	A	O	G	L	I
O	C	D	Z	G	U	E	I	R	T	Q	Y	C
O	E	A	T	N	T	P	P	F	K	E	S	A
H	G	M	E	M	A	L	F	A	O	E	U	L

AFLAME	HYSTERICAL	PROD
AGITATE	IGNITE	SUSCITATE
DISTURB	IMPEL	SWAY
FIRE	INCITE	TEASE
FRANTIC	MOVE	TITILLATE
GOAD	PERK UP	WIND UP

"Change the way you look
at things, and the things
you look at change."

Wayne Dyer

110   Maze

Start at the top and find a path to the middle of the maze.

"Standing or walking, sitting or lying down, during all these waking hours, let him establish mindfulness of good will, which men call the highest state!"

Buddha

Matching Pairs

Can you identify six matching pairs of butterflies? Matching pairs are identical in every detail.

112   **Arroword**

Solve the clues, then enter each answer in the direction of the arrows, one letter per square. When completed, the letters in shaded squares can be rearranged to form another word.

			▼				▼	
Chanel, fashion designer	Opaque gem	Gambling place		Temporary police force	Agitate	Wrong		Told fibs
⌐	▼	▼		Raised platform ►	▼	▼		
Hobby ►								Come to a halt
Equine animal ►				Face ►				▼
⌐							Stretch	
Cus-tomers	According to the time-piece		Comment	Employed ►			▼	
⌐	▼		▼	Cut (the lawn, for example)		Compare		Mas-culine
Room access		Insignia ►		▼		▼		▼
⌐					Large monkey		Slippery fish	
Famous American battle		Rouse ►			▼		▼	
⌐				Pare ►				
Mark of a wound		In an eager way ►						

Sudoku

Place one of the numbers from 1 to 9 into every empty cell so that each row, each column and each 3x3 block contains all the numbers from 1 to 9.

	3	9	5				6	
	1		6		2	4		
			1	4		5	7	
7				6	9			1
8	9						4	7
6			4	7				3
	7	4		3	6			
		5	9		8		2	
	2				4	3	9	

"Pay more attention to compassion and you'll find you're happier. It's that practical and simple."

Dalai Lama

114   Codeword

Every letter in this puzzle has been replaced by a number, the number remaining the same for that letter wherever it occurs. Every letter of the alphabet has been used. Substitute numbers for letters to complete the codeword.

It may help to cross off the letters beneath the grid to keep a track of progress, and to use the reference box showing which numbers have been decoded. Three letters have already been entered into the grid, to help you on your way.

26	19	24	11	8	7		21	17	7	4	20	22	7	4
7			8		17		5			23		7		12
19	14	3	20	16	19	24	16		4	10	18	18	8	7
17			16		4		19	9	7			18		7
14	7	6	16		7 E	19 A	16 T		17	7	13	19	24	16
	8		5		17		5	6	6			24		22
19	22	5	24	11	4	16		19	4	16	17	10	14	7
1		21		24		10	24	23		10		24		19
20	24	7	1	20	19	8		7	4	13	25	7	19	16
19		17			8	7	16		25		10		11	
21	7	19	24	20	16		25	5	7		17	25	7	19
8		16			19	2	7		19		4			20
19	16	5	24	7	17		5	26	16	17	20	14	7	14
24		17		15		17		25		16			10
7	19	4	16	7	17	8	2		7	9	7	22	21	16

A B C D E F G H I J K L M

N O P Q R S T U V W X Y Z

1	2	3	4	5	6	7 E	8	9	10	11	12	13
14	15	16 T	17	18	19 A	20	21	22	23	24	25	26

115   Wordsearch: Dressmaking

Can you find all of the listed words hidden in the grid below?
Words run horizontally, vertically or diagonally, in either a forward or
backward direction.

U	N	E	Y	S	Q	A	N	O	T	T	U	B
L	B	S	Y	Q	L	Z	A	F	A	K	D	O
W	E	S	I	T	S	T	A	E	L	P	V	N
H	C	H	A	L	K	G	S	T	R	A	D	M
E	N	J	E	H	K	H	N	E	E	D	L	E
M	L	E	E	H	S	D	D	I	F	N	F	N
M	R	P	N	C	I	G	W	M	W	N	G	F
I	A	O	A	Z	I	N	S	A	S	E	F	A
N	Y	G	F	N	S	I	R	C	X	R	S	D
G	E	A	G	S	H	S	I	H	Y	E	A	E
V	Q	L	Q	S	S	S	L	I	Y	A	C	W
X	O	C	K	K	S	E	F	N	M	A	R	X
S	T	B	V	O	D	R	R	E	L	N	P	N
I	W	R	R	O	T	P	Z	D	I	W	Z	Q
N	O	S	M	H	M	W	A	K	S	M	S	F

BUTTON	HOOKS	PRESSING
CHALK	LACE	REELS
DARTS	MACHINE	SCISSORS
DRESS FORM	MODEL	SEWING
EDGING	NEEDLE	SILK
HEMMING	PLEAT	YARN

"Believe that life is worth living
and your belief will help
create the fact."

William James

Criss Cross: Picnic Hamper

The words are provided, but can you fit them all into the grid?

4 letters
BOWL
BUNS
PATE
WINE

5 letters
APPLE
BREAD
CAKES
FLASK
FORKS
FRUIT

PLATE
SALAD
WATER

6 letters
BANANA
COFFEE
GATEAU
HAMPER
KNIVES
OLIVES
PEPPER
SPOONS

7 letters
NAPKINS

8 letters
LEMONADE
SANDWICH
TOMATOES

9 letters
CORKSCREW

10 letters
MAYONNAISE

Flower Power

Fit the listed words into the grid below, then rearrange the letters in the shaded squares to form another word related to the theme of this book.

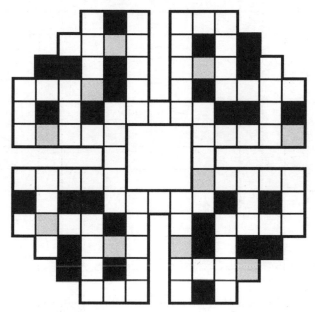

3 letters

ANY
APT
BOW
BUT
DEN
FEE
HOG
PAR

4 letters

BEAT
BEET
BRAY
CHEF
EDIT
FLEA

HERO
NEXT
REEL
TALK
WANT
ZINC

5 letters

ANGLE
BADGE
BEIGE
BEVEL
BRIEF
FALSE

FORCE
LOUSE
OCEAN
SEPIA
SHORT
TUTOR

"That's life: starting over, one breath at a time."

Sharon Salzberg

118

Maze

Start at the top and find a path to the middle of the maze.

"Holding on to anything is like
holding on to your breath.
You will suffocate. The only way
to get anything in the physical
universe is by letting go of it. Let
go, and it will be yours forever."

Deepak Chopra

119   Pyragram

Every clue in this puzzle is an anagram leading to a single-word solution. Correctly solve the anagram on each level of the pyramid and another word will appear, reading down the central column.

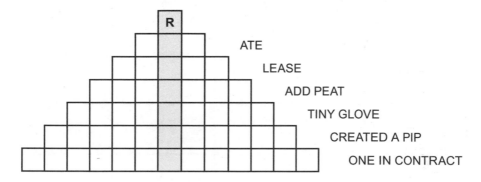

ATE

LEASE

ADD PEAT

TINY GLOVE

CREATED A PIP

ONE IN CONTRACT

120   Word Ladder

Change one letter at a time (but not the position of any letter) to make a new word – and move from the word at the top of the ladder to the word at the bottom using the exact number of rungs provided.

121   Arroword

Solve the clues, then enter each answer in the direction of the arrows, one letter per square. When completed, the letters in shaded squares can be rearranged to form another word.

Adult insect	▼	High, lofty	Excava-tions	▼	Noise made by a snake	Humble	▼	Stony waste matter
Thorough physical examina-tion ▶		▼	▼			▼		Defunct
Bloc ▶					Having negative qualities ▶			▼
Prevents from speaking out ▶				Grow old ▶				
▶				Expert who studies data	Land-locked republic in north-west Africa		Not either	
Vacations (abbr)	Organic com-ponent of soil		Remedy ▶	▼	▼		▼	
Reddish-brown dye used mostly on hair ▶	▼					Distinctive period of time		___ pole, tribal emblem
▶			Awake	▶			▼	▼
Partially opened flower		Precious or semi-precious stone	Impudent or insolent rejoinder	▶			Plural of the word 'am'	
Deficient in beauty ▶		▼			Cereal grass ▶		▼	
▶			Legal capital of Bolivia	▶				
Con-sumption	Annual road-worthiness test (inits) ▶				Border ▶			

122 Wordsearch: I Meant to Do My Work Today

Can you find all of the underlined words from the poem "I Meant to Do My Work Today" by Richard Le Gallienne? Words run forward or backward, in either a horizontal, vertical, or diagonal direction.

```
G E Y E P L G N I L L A C
N A H L U W H A T E A H L
I G W P F B E A A L P L G
S E R P C R I V N S A E N
S M E A N T E R J D I A I
O A N E S S B T D N A L N
T C E W A S A Y T N U W I
D R D R O T E N W U S C H
T O L E A R C S G I B R S
V S A K T I B N G I N B T
T S U R F T N H E R F D D
O T G O O D I B G R I N L
D V H W F N R L O E E R U
A F E Y G Y V V F W L A O
Y O M R F D L E H E D W C
```

I <u>meant</u> to do my <u>work</u> <u>today</u> –

But a <u>brown</u> <u>bird</u> <u>sang</u> in the <u>apple</u> <u>tree</u>,

And a <u>butterfly</u> <u>flitted</u> <u>across</u> the <u>field</u>,

And <u>all</u> the <u>leaves</u> were <u>calling</u> me.

And the <u>wind</u> went <u>sighing</u> <u>over</u> the <u>land</u>,

<u>Tossing</u> the <u>grasses</u> to and <u>fro</u>,

And a <u>rainbow</u> <u>held</u> out its <u>shining</u> <u>hand</u> –

So <u>what</u> <u>could</u> I do but <u>laugh</u> and go?

123   Codeword

Every letter in this puzzle has been replaced by a number, the number remaining the same for that letter wherever it occurs. Every letter of the alphabet has been used. Substitute numbers for letters to complete the codeword.

It may help to cross off the letters beneath the grid to keep a track of progress, and to use the reference box showing which numbers have been decoded. Three letters have already been entered into the grid, to help you on your way.

2		24		2	8 P	21 A	26 L	16	17	4	16	1	4	16
6	19	23	16	5		11		16		10		21		
17		1		5	19	16	20	22	16	1	25	23	1	9
25	19	16	17	17		19		3		19		21		
19		17		14		17	8	16	4	25	21	4	26	16
22		13	2	2	5		21		21			26		26
4	22	16		19			26		17		13	16	19	16
25		16		16	17	4	21	8	16	3		21		4
23	24	8	17		23		11			23		1	2	25
11		16			10		16		21	17	12	17		19
16	1	19	21	8	25	22	19	16		24		14		2
	2		18		23			26		21	11	21	23	26
3	2	4	22	24	16	1	25	21	19	15		11		15
	17		19		25			1		16	7	16	4	25
26	16	11	16	26	14	16	21	3	16	3		1		16

A B C D E F G H I J K L M

N O P Q R S T U V W X Y Z

1	2	3	4	5	6	7	8 P	9	10	11	12	13
14	15	16	17	18	19	20	21 A	22	23	24	25	26 L

124   Sudoku

Place one of the numbers from 1 to 9 into every empty cell so that each row, each column and each 3x3 block contains all the numbers from 1 to 9.

	9			5			1	
	2	8		3		5	7	
1			2		6			8
	1	4	3		2	9	5	
2			9		5			4
	6	5	4		8	2	3	
7			6		4			5
	8	2		9		7	4	
	4			2			6	

"You have brains in your head.
You have feet in your shoes.
You can steer yourself any
direction you choose."

Dr Seuss

125   Criss Cross: Soft Words

The words are provided, but can you fit them all into the grid?

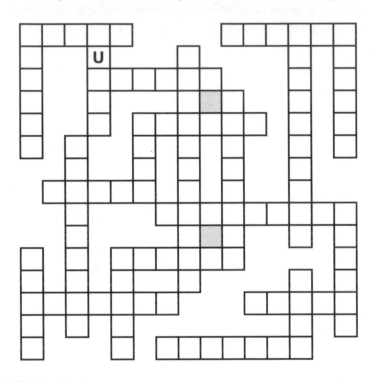

4 letters
KIND
MILD

5 letters
BALMY
BLAND
CUSHY
MISTY
MUSHY
QUIET

6 letters
BUTTER
CLOUDS
DULCET
MELLOW
SILKEN
SMOOTH
TENDER

7 letters
RELAXED
SQUASHY

8 letters
SOAPSUDS

9 letters
LUXURIOUS
MELODIOUS

10 letters
COTTON WOOL

11 letters
MELLIFLUOUS

126   In Place

Place the listed words horizontally into the grid, so that when read from top left to bottom right, the letters in the shaded squares spell out a word linked to the theme of this book. Some letters are already in place.

COMFORT

HORIZON

IMAGINE

ONESELF

SNUGGLE

THOUGHT

WISTFUL

"What we are today comes
from our thoughts of yesterday,
and present thoughts build
our life of tomorrow: our life is
the creation of our mind."

Buddha

127   **Maze**

Start at the top and find a path to the middle of the maze.

"People usually consider walking on water or in thin air a miracle. But I think the real miracle is not to walk either on water or in thin air, but to walk on earth. Every day we are engaged in a miracle which we don't even recognize: a blue sky, white clouds, green leaves, the black, curious eyes of a child—our own two eyes. All is a miracle."

Thich Nhat Hanh

128   Wordsearch: Beekeeping

Can you find all of the listed words hidden in the grid below?
Words run horizontally, vertically or diagonally, in either a forward or
backward direction.

```
D Y L L E J L A Y O R I Y
D N U G W B S E E Q Q H I
K A G A R D E N M S Y I A
I S H U M M I N G A S V E
O X R D I F P N R R R E G
K O Q S E T I M Y D F F Y
A K D E T W A F E C L N P
N L L R X R G G P R O H N
F E A A A I T B J S W O E
D I L R P T A W Q A E D J
M N L L V I C P Y U R O G
L S S D O A A E T O S O E
L E D U T P E R N C G F A
O C B R O O D E Y V E I L
R T R E N R C D L D O C D
```

APIARY	FRAME	MITES
BROOD	GARDEN	NECTAR
DRONE	HIVE	POLLEN
EGGS	HUMMING	ROYAL JELLY
FLOWERS	INSECT	VEIL
FOOD	LARVAE	WINGS

"If my life is going to mean anything, I have to live it myself."

Rick Riordan

129   Arroword

Solve the clues, then enter each answer in the direction of the arrows, one letter per square. When completed, the letters in shaded squares can be rearranged to form another word.

Native of Bangkok, for example ▼		Church instrument ▼		Scottish lake ▼		Relish of chopped pickled cucumbers ▼	Province of Indonesia
Ruffian ►		▼					
Bow ►				God of thunder		Large grassy plain	Haemorrhage
►				▼		▼	▼
Entertainment venue	Overwhelming feeling of wonder		Conforming to Islamic dietary laws ►				
African republic, capital Luanda ►	▼					Popular number puzzle ▼	
Held back	No longer fashionable	Use water to remove soap ►					
└	▼		At high volume ►				
Constellation, the Little Bear	Shortened boy's name	Every one	Swab		Overworked horse		Informer
└	▼	▼	▼		▼		▼
Capital of Norway ►				Alias (inits) ►			
Bark in a high-pitched tone ►				Intestine ►			

Sudoku

Place one of the numbers from 1 to 9 into every empty cell so that each row, each column and each 3x3 block contains all the numbers from 1 to 9.

	7		9		3	2		
5				1			9	
	2	1	7		8	4		
7	6				5	3		
		9		8		1		
		8	2				4	9
		5	8		7	9	6	
	3			4				2
		2	6		1		5	

"Joy is what happens to us when we allow ourselves to recognize how good things really are."

Marianne Williamson

Codeword

Every letter in this puzzle has been replaced by a number, the number remaining the same for that letter wherever it occurs. Every letter of the alphabet has been used. Substitute numbers for letters to complete the codeword.

It may help to cross off the letters beneath the grid to keep a track of progress, and to use the reference box showing which numbers have been decoded. Three letters have already been entered into the grid, to help you on your way.

17	1	6	6		22	16	9	1	16		9	14	11	9
22			1	26	6		19		5			9		7
				I	T	S								
12	15	5	18		5	10	19	16	24	19		22		25
12			26		24		10			2	5	6	26	19
		20	7	26	19		19	26	2	17			4	
23	22	19		1		21		25		14	16	1	14	16
1		17		2	17	19	4	19	23			24		19
6	17	5	16	13		26		11		6	14	16	5	25
2		15			19	6	2	14	25	26		14		10
14	12	12	19	25		5		25		14		25	14	19
	15			1	5	11	20		2	5	6	19		
3	22	5	1	15			25		15		9			9
22		25		19	25	25	5	26	5		25	5	26	19
1		1			5		4		6	19	5			5
8	19	5	15		26	22	15	1	9		26	5	2	13

A B C D E F G H I J K L M
N O P Q R S T U V W X Y Z

1	2	3	4	5	6	7	8	9	10	11	12	13
I					S							
14	15	16	17	18	19	20	21	22	23	24	25	26
												T

Jigsaw

Which four shapes (two black and two white) can be fitted together to form the watering can shown here? The pieces may be rotated, but not flipped over.

A

B

C

D

E

F

G

H

I

J

K

L

M

N

O

133   Criss Cross: Floral Clock

The words are provided, but can you fit them all into the grid?

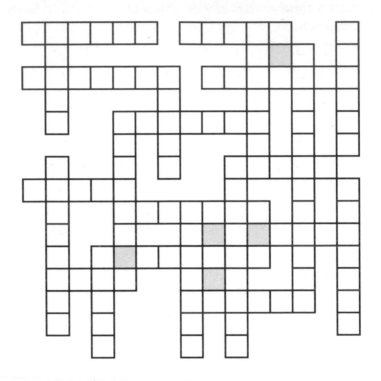

4 letters	6 letters	PANSIES
FLAX	EDGING	SHAPING
SAGE	FORMAL	WEEDING
	GRAVEL	
5 letters	IBERIS	8 letters
AGAVE	SALVIA	FEVERFEW
HANDS		
HOURS	7 letters	9 letters
SEDUM	ALYSSUM	HOUSE LEEK
SLOPE	BEDDING	
THYME	FLOWERS	12 letters
	MODESTO	NIAGARA PARKS

134   Wordsearch: Hiking Gear

Can you find all of the listed words hidden in the grid below?
Words run horizontally, vertically or diagonally, in either a forward or
backward direction.

P	P	K	D	L	T	E	B	L	J	J	B	W
S	R	A	L	U	C	O	N	I	B	L	Q	A
F	T	R	C	T	O	N	Y	R	A	Q	N	T
F	R	X	E	T	I	F	G	N	N	S	I	E
X	F	A	S	Q	O	Y	K	L	U	K	I	R
Z	W	J	C	O	E	E	S	N	O	C	A	F
K	L	H	D	S	T	R	G	S	E	V	Z	L
O	P	L	I	S	E	L	Y	L	T	T	E	A
S	K	C	O	S	A	C	L	U	I	C	I	S
T	H	J	E	S	T	P	E	N	A	A	E	H
R	A	D	S	W	H	L	D	M	Z	H	F	L
H	T	E	M	O	S	I	E	T	C	W	I	I
R	S	A	N	D	L	R	N	T	Q	Q	N	G
X	P	E	I	J	A	F	A	I	P	S	K	H
O	K	S	A	L	F	M	U	U	C	A	V	T

BINOCULARS	FOOD	SCARF
BLANKET	GLOVES	SOCKS
BOOTS	HAT	SUNGLASSES
CAMERA	KNIFE	VACUUM FLASK
CELL PHONE	MAP	WATER
FLASHLIGHT	MATCHES	WHISTLE

"You don't have to be great to start, but you have to start to be great."

Zig Ziglar

135   Maze

Start at the top and find a path to the middle of the maze.

"Flow with whatever may happen and let your mind be free: Stay centered by accepting whatever you are doing. This is the ultimate."

Zhuang Zhou

136   Pyragram

Every clue in this puzzle is an anagram leading to a single-word solution. Correctly solve the anagram on each level of the pyramid and another word will appear, reading down the central column.

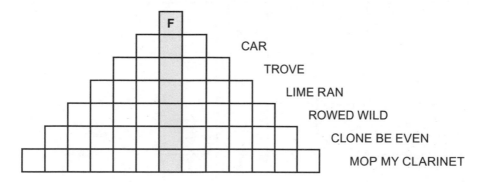

CAR

TROVE

LIME RAN

ROWED WILD

CLONE BE EVEN

MOP MY CLARINET

137   Word Wheel

How many words of three or more letters can you make from those in the wheel, without using plurals, abbreviations or proper nouns?

The central letter must appear once in every word and no letter in a section of the wheel may be used more than once.

There is at least one nine-letter word in the wheel.

Nine-letter word(s):

_____

138   Arroword

Solve the clues, then enter each answer in the direction of the arrows, one letter per square. When completed, the letters in shaded squares can be rearranged to form another word.

Decide upon	▼	Projection at the end of a piece of wood	▼	Left-hand page	___ Espana!	▼	Give up	▼
⌐								
Equine speed contest (5,4)		Harangue		Flightless bird	Hard outer layer of a fruit		Law-breaking	
⌐		▼		▼	▼		▼	
Girl's name ▶						Grotesque		Payment required for not fulfilling a contract
Local time at the 0 meridian (inits)	Made a noise like a cow		Square, not trendy	▶		▼		
⌐	▼		Cone-bearing tree	US coin ▶				
Leaves		Com-munist state of Asia	▼	Primitive, mainly aquatic organism	Lair	▶		
⌐		▼		▼			Fluid used for writing	
British nobleman	▶				Anoint or lubricate	▶	▼	
⌐			Cada-verous	▶				
Artificial language, a simplifi-cation of Esperanto	Body of water	▶			Where the sun shines and the stars twinkle!	▶		

139   **Sudoku**

Place one of the numbers from 1 to 9 into every empty cell so that each row, each column and each 3x3 block contains all the numbers from 1 to 9.

6	8	4				9	5	1
		1			5	8		
2				1	6			3
		6	1					7
	4		2		8		9	
5					3	4		
4			9	7				5
		2	6			3		
9	6	7				?	8	4

"It's never too late—never too late to start over, never too late to be happy."

Jane Fonda

140   Codeword

Every letter in this puzzle has been replaced by a number, the number remaining the same for that letter wherever it occurs. Every letter of the alphabet has been used. Substitute numbers for letters to complete the codeword.

It may help to cross off the letters beneath the grid to keep a track of progress, and to use the reference box showing which numbers have been decoded. Three letters have already been entered into the grid, to help you on your way.

18	13	17	6	19	■	17	7	17	9	24	8	2	15	17
17	■	25	■	8	■	6	■	22	■	17	■	■	■	6
20	8	17	20	20	17	7	24	8	■	16	15	9	6	19
17	■	2	■	13	■	8	■	26	■	8	■	5	■	8
9	17	2	2	15	8	■	26	5	15	4	4	9	8	22
3	■	■	■	7	■	22	■	17	■	13	■	9	■	■
11	19	8	25	8	■	8	17	11	2	■	22	17	15	2
15	■	20	■	2	■	23	■	8	■	8	■	4	■	11
6	19	13	18	■	14	8	9	9	■	12	13	3	8	20 R
■	■	11	■	4	■	6	■	3	■	12	■	■	■	17 A
2	11	15	9	8	11	11	13	■	4	5	20	22	8	7 N
25	■	6	■	6	■	8	■	4	■	2	■	20	■	24
17	4	17	6	10	■	22	8	13	1	15	22	15	2	8
2	■	■	■	13	■	9	■	9	■	21	■	9	■	2
19	17	6	10	7	8	3	8	22	■	8	6	9	17	11

A   B   C   D   E   F   G   H   I   J   K   L   M

N   O   P   Q   R   S   T   U   V   W   X   Y   Z

1	2	3	4	5	6	7 N	8	9	10	11	12	13
14	15	16	17 A	18	19	20 R	21	22	23	24	25	26

141   Wordsearch: Bodies of Water

Can you find all of the listed words hidden in the grid below?
Words run horizontally, vertically or diagonally, in either a forward or
backward direction.

```
Y D O N B Y A B K L A P U
A T Y G T E L L W V Z J A
B R N L S Z A H T R T E K
N H W D R E I E A T S N H
O N E Z B T A E S A R A K
S R D R E Y J O C L E A A
D B D S A U A C F S A E V
U L E I U I U B O A S R K
H A L H F L R R L H Z D A
Y C L W O T O I T E D O A
O K S M R K M R S J I R V
S S E A T H O L B H I K H
I E A D S N B A S S S E A
G A O C E L E B E S S E A
A E S N A M S A T I S Y A
```

ARAL SEA	IRISH SEA	PALK BAY
BASS SEA	KARA SEA	RED SEA
BEAUFORT SEA	KIEL BAY	SEA OF AZOV
BLACK SEA	KORO SEA	TASMAN SEA
CELEBES SEA	MOLUCCA SEA	WEDDELL SEA
HUDSON BAY	NORTH SEA	WHITE SEA

"Motivation is what gets you started. Habit is what keeps you going."

Jim Ryun

142   Criss Cross: Tea

The words are provided, but can you fit them all into the grid?

5 letters
ASSAM
CHINA
GREEN
HUNAN
INDIA
JAPAN

6 letters
CEYLON
DOOARS
HERBAL

7 letters
CHUN MEE
RUSSIAN

8 letters
CAMEROON
HAPUTALE
MATURATA
NINGCHOW

9 letters
GUNPOWDER
INDONESIA
MATCHA UJI
RATNAPURA
SPIDER LEG

10 letters
DARJEELING

143   Flower Power

Fit the listed words into the grid below, then rearrange the letters in the shaded squares to form another word related to the theme of this book.

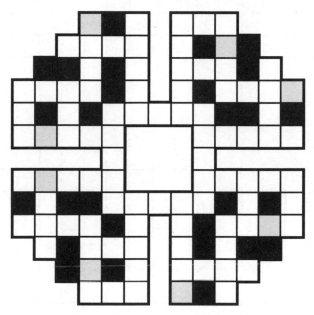

3 letters	4 letters		5 letters	
ART	AMEN	KNIT	AMBER	MEDIA
AWN	BENT	MALT	CAPER	MYRRH
BOO	DEBT	MINX	CHAOS	OFTEN
CUB	FREE	NONE	HALVE	PROXY
DIP	GOAT	RIND	HOUSE	STERN
NUT	JERK	TORN	MARSH	VISTA
SPA				
TON				

"Fear is a natural reaction to moving closer to the truth."

Pema Chodron

144   Maze

Start at the top and find a path to the middle of the maze.

"When I dare to be powerful—
to use my strength in the
service of my vision, then it
becomes less and less important
whether I am afraid."

Audre Lorde

145   **Sudoku**

Place one of the numbers from 1 to 9 into every empty cell so that each row, each column and each 3x3 block contains all the numbers from 1 to 9.

	1	2			7			5
4		9	2	3				7
		3			8		9	
		7		8			3	6
	8		7		2		4	
2	9			4		5		
	2		6			1		
5				1	3	6		9
6			9			7	8	

"The more you praise and celebrate your life, the more there is in life to celebrate."

Oprah Winfrey

146 Arroword

Solve the clues, then enter each answer in the direction of the arrows, one letter per square. When completed, the letters in shaded squares can be rearranged to form another word.

Strong washing solution ▼		Naughtily or annoyingly playful ▼		Item of cutlery	Demesne	▼	Change course	Pigpen
Exclamation of joy or victory ▶		▼			▼		Tubular pasta filled with meat or cheese	▼
▶				Faction ▶			▼	
Office note	Assume or act the character of ▶							
▶				Sharply		Type of cobra		Division of a week
Alike	Shed tears		Bear ▶	▼		▼		▼
Body of water to the east of Finland (5,3) ▶	▼							
Guard to confine falling coals to a hearth		Fiddling Roman emperor	Feat	One of the strands twisted together to make yarn ▶				
▶		▼	▼			Angry		Cashpoint (inits)
Quick look ▶				Extinct flightless bird of New Zealand ▶		▼		▼
Morose	Dependent ▶							
▶					Darken ▶			

Wordsearch: Herbs

Can you find all of the listed words hidden in the grid below?
Words run horizontally, vertically or diagonally, in either a forward or
backward direction.

```
P E M I L K T H I S T L E
H T U R T S Q Y N E O H W
E N Q R Q N O G A R R A T
P I I B R E P A C C K K A
E M J O O G E T A I E E G
N R O Z P R G R P E A S M
N A M K H G A D R D D I L
Y E T W T W S G R L I N A
R P R D A E U S E D O A B
O S A Y V N R W O L E A N
Y P S I E D W U M R S D O
A M H F G P F E A I R E M
L C A T A E D E L S R E E
O E U C E C H I C O R Y L
S S V G E L I M O M A C K
```

ANISE	CHICORY	PENNYROYAL
BASIL	CHIVES	RUE
BORAGE	FENUGREEK	SAGE
CAMOMILE	LEMON BALM	SORREL
CAPER	MACE	SPEARMINT
CARAWAY	MILK THISTLE	TARRAGON

"At the end of the day, let there be no excuses, no explanations, no regrets."

Steve Maraboli

148   Codeword

Every letter in this puzzle has been replaced by a number, the number remaining the same for that letter wherever it occurs. Every letter of the alphabet has been used. Substitute numbers for letters to complete the codeword.

It may help to cross off the letters beneath the grid to keep a track of progress, and to use the reference box showing which numbers have been decoded. Three letters have already been entered into the grid, to help you on your way.

23	21	3	10	15	14	21	9	20		8	21	3	9	20
20		11		2		3		5		12		24		9
21	17	5	20	2		9 T	21 A	5 B	6	20	21	11		12
3		26		11		20		3		14		21		15
9	2	11	17	4	20	2	19		12	20	10	9	15	10
		1		9			1		7					21
3	8	15	13		17	21	14	21	13	20	2	15	21	6
14		10		13		7		16		2		14		6
25	7	20	2	6	25	25	22	20	1		3	20	18	19
8				20		8				23		6		
23	25	2	17	21	6		21	3	4	15	2	21	14	9
6		21		17		3		20		14		3		12
21		5	6	15	14	22	20	2		15	14	9	20	2
22		5		14		15		7		3		15		20
20	22	15	14	13		9	25	25	9	12	21	10	12	20

A B C D E F G H I J K L M

N O P Q R S T U V W X Y Z

| 1 | 2 | 3 | 4 | 5 B | 6 | 7 | 8 | 9 T | 10 | 11 | 12 | 13 |
| 14 | 15 | 16 | 17 | 18 | 19 | 20 | 21 A | 22 | 23 | 24 | 25 | 26 |

Odd One Out

All of these beachballs have been thrown around a little, but you should still be able to spot which is different from the rest.

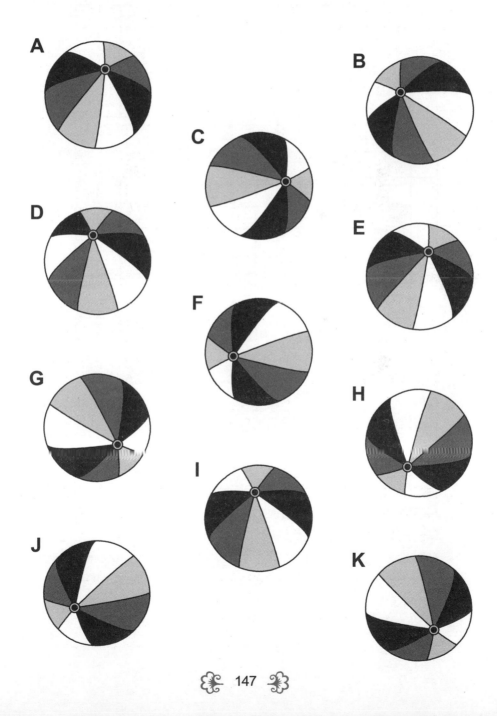

A

B

C

D

E

F

G

H

I

J

K

150   Criss Cross: In the Park

The words are provided, but can you fit them all into the grid?

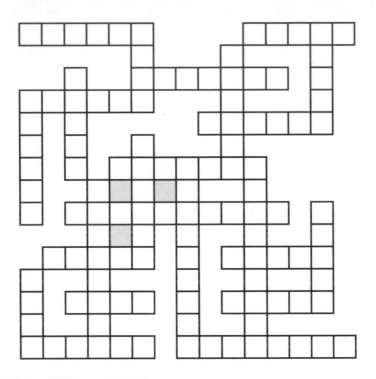

4 letters
CAFE
KIDS
LAKE

5 letters
GRASS
PATHS
PONDS
ROSES
SEATS
SWANS
TREES

6 letters
PEOPLE
PICNIC
SHRUBS
SPORTS
STATUE
SWINGS
TENNIS

7 letters
BENCHES
FLOWERS

8 letters
FOUNTAIN
FRESH AIR

9 letters
CRAZY GOLF
SQUIRRELS

10 letters
ROUNDABOUT

151   Shadow Play

Which of the shadows is that of the cyclist shown here?

A

B

C

D

E

F

G

152 Maze

Start at the top and find a path to the middle of the maze.

"Real integrity is doing the right thing, knowing that nobody's going to know whether you did it or not."

Oprah Winfrey

153 Wordsearch: Musical Instruments

Can you find all of the listed words hidden in the grid below?
Words run horizontally, vertically or diagonally, in either a forward or
backward direction.

```
H W F E V Y W G O C D N D
T E I L Q C S F U R Q D L
O W S D I E T L O I G B F
N V R D M X E H L B T A E
N U T I L T C N Z E O A N
M A H F U I D H C T B E R
L C T L V E T B D S M E A
D E O A G B W M E W Q A Q
N I L L R N V W A F Z E J
S C S M O E O H O G I L T
X H O C B C S G N E K F K
S O T I A H C U A N N F G
G Z A S T Y Y I I M C I S
M S E P I P N A P O F H A
T N O Z E K S R U U T W D
```

BELL

CHIMES

CLAVICHORD

DRUM

FIDDLE

FIFE

GONG

GUITAR

LUTE

MOOG

OBOE

ORGAN

PAN PIPES

PIANO

PICCOLO

SHAWM

TABOR

WHIFFLE

"Do not wait to strike till the iron is hot; but make it hot by striking."

William Butler Yeats

154   Arroword

Solve the clues, then enter each answer in the direction of the arrows, one letter per square. When completed, the letters in shaded squares can be rearranged to form another word.

Part of a church which contains the altar ▼		Check accounts ▼		Container for ashes ▼		Living in ▼		Aviator
Suffering delusions of perse-cution ▶		▼						
Earth's nearest star ▶				Bathroom fixtures		Burdened		Requires
⚑			Bird of prey's claw ▼		▼		▼	
Crimson	Boy child		Ease up ▶					
Foolish ▶	▼						Herb with leaves valued as salad greens ▼	
Against		Item of dining room furniture	Warhorse ▶					
⬎		▼		Hostelries ▶				
Waxy animal substance used in perfume	Chart		Hour at which something is due (inits)	Decay		Gentle blow		Division of an ocean
⬎	▼		▼	▼		▼		▼
High male voice ▶					Rever-ential salutation ▶			
Vegetable matter used as a fuel ▶				Round vegetable ▶				

155   Sudoku

Place one of the numbers from 1 to 9 into every empty cell so that each row, each column and each 3x3 block contains all the numbers from 1 to 9.

					2	9	6	4
8		5	9					3
	9		4	1		7		
6				9		2	1	
7			3		1			6
	5	4		2				9
		1		3	6		4	
4					5	8		2
5	7	2	8					

"You will face many defeats in life, but never let yourself be defeated."

Maya Angelou

156   Codeword

Every letter in this puzzle has been replaced by a number, the number remaining the same for that letter wherever it occurs. Every letter of the alphabet has been used. Substitute numbers for letters to complete the codeword.

It may help to cross off the letters beneath the grid to keep a track of progress, and to use the reference box showing which numbers have been decoded. Three letters have already been entered into the grid, to help you on your way.

7	5	26	1	16	24	■	15	■	18	■	12	7	18	19
9	■	1	■	24	■	4	14	11	26	19	22	■	■	7
9	1	7	23	23	3	24	21	■	15	■	14	1	26	6
14	■	2	■	25	■	11	■	10	14	9	19	■	■	19
19	6	24	25	9	9	14	7	25	■	■	9	24	18	7
■	14	■	■	■	3	■	■	20	25	13	19	■	■	6
16	7	13	5	2	7	1	1	24	11	■	24	11	13	14
■	13	■	11	■	6	■	24	■	26	■	11	■	22	■
9	22	24	24	■	9	25	16	7	17	25	14	24	25	9
8	■	■	12	14	14	3	■	■	25	■	■	6	■	■
6	14	14	23	■	■	24	16	9	14	6	15	7	11	19
26	■	■	14	7	6	11	■	14	■	26	■	16	■	7
11	14	14	20	■	7	■	20	7	26	11	19	26	14	6
2	■	■	2	7 **A**	6 **R**	19 **T**	14	6	■	20	■	20	■	24
14	3	14	14	■	14	■	11	■	7	9	3	14	13	19

A B C D E F G H I J K L M
N O P Q R S T U V W X Y Z

1	2	3	4	5	6 **R**	7 **A**	8	9	10	11	12	13
14	15	16	17	18	19 **T**	20	21	22	23	24	25	26

157   Pyragram

Every clue in this puzzle is an anagram leading to a single-word solution. Correctly solve the anagram on each level of the pyramid and another word will appear, reading down the central column.

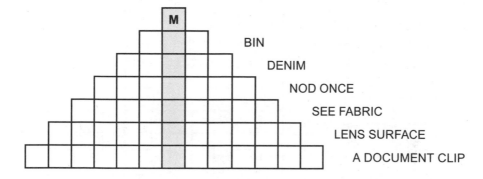

BIN

DENIM

NOD ONCE

SEE FABRIC

LENS SURFACE

A DOCUMENT CLIP

158   Word Ladder

Change one letter at a time (but not the position of any letter) to make a new word – and move from the word at the top of the ladder to the word at the bottom using the exact number of rungs provided.

159   Criss Cross: Warm Words

The words are provided, but can you fit them all into the grid?

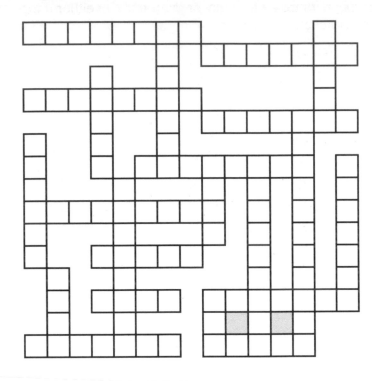

3 letters	6 letters	8 letters
GAS	SULTRY	FEVERISH
		KEROSENE
4 letters	**7 letters**	LUKEWARM
COAL	FLUSHED	PARAFFIN
FIRE	GLOWING	
OVEN	HEATING	**9 letters**
	PASSION	EIDERDOWN
	RADIATE	TEMPERATE
5 letters	SUMMERY	
BALMY		**11 letters**
COVER		ELECTRICITY
SUNNY		
TEPID		

160   Wordsearch: Canine Friends

Can you find all of the listed words hidden in the grid below?
Words run horizontally, vertically or diagonally, in either a forward or
backward direction.

```
R H A I N B Y F R X T H V
H L P T B M C O K X C L I
H Z E Z L O Y A L T Y J L
P C T N H C I L I L N E M
L W T I N C O B E L E I Q
E A I E H E M L B H N A A
H L N S F C K C L I G Q D
W K G W H J O X G A V Q U
D S S E P O E I E P R E T
U H S H R O W L I E N D T
B S N C I N R I W D V O P
T U O H Y H U E N O Z N V
G R O W L I N G R G B V E
G B D X S T I U C S I B O
X Q N C Z L T R S R Q E L
```

BISCUITS	COMB	LOYALTY
BITCH	FETCH	PETTING
BOWL	GROWLING	SHOWING
BRUSH	HEEL	VET
CHEWS	KENNEL	WALKS
COLLAR	LEAD	WHELP

"You can't stop the waves, but you can learn to surf."

Jon Kabat-Zinn

161   Maze

Start at the top and find a path to the middle of the maze.

"The mind in its natural state can be compared to the sky, covered by layers of cloud which hide its true nature."

Kalu Rinpoche

162   Spot the Difference

In each of the pictures below, there is one detail different from the other pictures. Can you spot the one difference in every case?

163   Arroword

Solve the clues, then enter each answer in the direction of the arrows, one letter per square. When completed, the letters in shaded squares can be rearranged to form another word.

Magnetic metallic element, symbol Fe	Gown	Sung dramas	▼	Links together	Puts a name to	At liberty	▼	Sharpen (a blade)
►	▼	▼		Hole for a coin ►	▼	▼		
Personal belief or judgment ►								Unhappy
Wager ►			Departs ►				▼	
►							Novel, fresh	
People	Line on a weather map		Most recent	Fourth largest of the Great Lakes ►			▼	
►	▼		▼	▼	Despatch	Cocktail fruit		In a bashful way
Church passage		Pointers ►			▼			▼
►					Fish eggs		Chap	
American raccoon	In a spooky manner ►				▼		▼	
►				Egg-shaped ►				
Overtake	Of textiles, having a rough surface ►							

164   Sudoku

Place one of the numbers from 1 to 9 into every empty cell so that each row, each column and each 3x3 block contains all the numbers from 1 to 9.

1	7	9				5	8	6
4				6	1			3
		6			8	7		
		1	6					2
	9		4		7		5	
8					3	9		
		4	1			3		
9			5	2				8
5	1	2				4	7	9

"Happiness is your nature.
It is not wrong to desire it.
What is wrong is seeking it
outside when it is inside."

Ramana Maharshi

165

Codeword

Every letter in this puzzle has been replaced by a number, the number remaining the same for that letter wherever it occurs. Every letter of the alphabet has been used. Substitute numbers for letters to complete the codeword.

It may help to cross off the letters beneath the grid to keep a track of progress, and to use the reference box showing which numbers have been decoded. Three letters have already been entered into the grid, to help you on your way.

11	18	16	10	11	■	26	6	7	13	20	5	18	4	3
10 T	■	17		9		17		23		23		■		13
6 A	4	13	4	5	1	13	21	11	■	8	13	7	3	18
7 R		12		17		5		18		6		21		4
22	6	4	20	18	10	■	22	17	18	4	9	18	4	3
13		■		3	■	12		18		10		4	■	
6	12	6	11	19		6	1	23	4	■	19	13	17	20
7		23		10		17		4		8	■	21		23
20	18	7	10	■	22	17	13	8		13	6	11	18	11
■		13		16	■	16		23		15		■		8
20	18	11	8	18	26	17	23	■	25	21	3	3	17	23
18	■	13		23		13		1		23		7	■	4
24	13	17	10	11		12	7	18	11	10	22	6	4	20
13	■		10		23		4		7		2	■	23	
10	23	11	10	6	10	7	18	14		5	18	23	17	20

A B C D E F G H I J K L M
N O P Q R S T U V W X Y Z

1	2	3	4	5	6	7	8	9	10	11	12	13
					A	R			T			

14	15	16	17	18	19	20	21	22	23	24	25	26

166   Jigsaw

Which four shapes (two black and two white) can be fitted together to form the dove shown here? The pieces may be rotated, but not flipped over.

167   Criss Cross: Trees and Shrubs

The words are provided, but can you fit them all into the grid?

3 letters
YEW

4 letters
ACER
BALM
LIME
PEAR
PLUM

5 letters
ASPEN
BALSA
BIRCH

HAZEL
LEMON
MANGO
OSIER
TAXUS
THUJA
TULIP

6 letters
BANANA
BRAZIL
GINKGO
ORANGE

7 letters
HEMLOCK
SPINDLE
WYCH-ELM

8 letters
HAWTHORN
MAHOGANY
SYCAMORE
WISTERIA

Reflections

Which of the designs below is an exact horizontal (left to right) mirror image of the design to the right?

I

2

3

4

5

6

7

8

Solutions

1

2

```
A W Y Z E N I H S N U S G
O S E V R E S E R P I R F
B U I U G Q H P H L E N L
O E M B N A Z B O D I S G
U L E U I M V Q I R T T R
S D H T L H V C M A C C J
T N P M I U E U O X E M Y
L U D W O S G G K X D T O
H B P U T K E E R A H S I
W R H U Q G T O P A O E Y
U T J R I E A S T C P D E
D R Y I N G B O C A S E K
D I E K O R L G D L M I S
R Y G D E H E N W B T O F
R D L H Z D S X T B F P T
```

3

```
  U     H   D
  G E N E   E L F
  L A U R E L   L
B I R D     I C E
    T E N A B L E
    H   U   E A T
D R E A M E R S
O N C E   A P T
T   T R O T   O
P A T I O   E G O
T   O U T L E T
B E A N S   Y E S
```

Answer: GRATITUDE

4

9	8	5	6	3	4	2	7	1
7	2	3	5	1	8	9	4	6
4	1	6	7	9	2	3	8	5
6	7	8	3	5	1	4	2	9
1	5	4	8	2	9	7	6	3
2	3	9	4	6	7	1	5	8
5	4	7	9	8	3	6	1	2
8	9	1	2	4	6	5	3	7
3	6	2	1	7	5	8	9	4

5

```
J O S T L E   F A N D A N G O
U   R   D   R   O   E     U
M A G A Z I N E   I N J E C T
B   G   T   A I R   D     S
O O Z E   I N K   A D R I F T
  W   D   O   Y E T   N   A
E N V Y I N G   P E P P E R Y
X   I   L   A W E   S     E
Q U E L L E D   E L A P S E D
U   W   A S H   O   E   L
I M P A I R   A N Y   T A M P
S   O   L O W   A   U     A
I D I O C Y   S I L E N C E R
T   N   A   E   T   I     T
E X T E R I O R   Y E A R L Y
```

6

F
One of the palm tree leaves is missing.

Solutions

7

```
A P P L E   D A T E   P L U M
    O     K     F         A
    M     P E R S I M M O N
  P E A C H   E     G   E   G
    G     U     T     D   O
L   R     C A R A M B O L A
E   A     K     M     A   L
M   N     L O G A N B E R R Y
O R A N G E   R       C
N   T     B   I   P K   H
    E     M E L O N   O L I V E
  L       R   D   M   W     E
  B I L B E R R Y   E   I
  M       Y   U G L I
  P E A R         O
```

8

9

10

```
        P
      D E W
    B A R E D
  G R A F T E D
W A N D E R I N G
A D V A N C E M E N T
B R A I N S T O R M I N G
```

11

The nine-letter word is:
HERBALIST

12

```
    B   D   S
M A G N A T E   G
  B     D I R T Y
P E T R O L E U M
    E     T     N
G R A P H   P E R
  E   A I D E   I
B A L L S   T A D
  D   F   R   F
T S A R   O A T H
  P E T T I E R
O B E Y   E R R S
```

Answer: ENERGY

13

8	3	9	2	6	4	1	5	7
5	4	2	1	3	7	6	9	8
7	1	6	8	9	5	2	4	3
3	2	7	5	1	6	9	8	4
9	6	5	7	4	8	3	2	1
1	8	4	3	2	9	7	6	5
4	5	3	6	7	2	8	1	9
6	7	8	9	5	1	4	3	2
2	9	1	4	8	3	5	7	6

Solutions

14

15

16

17

Answer: FORGIVENESS

18

19

1	8	4	5	9	3	2	7	6
5	6	2	1	7	4	8	9	3
9	3	7	2	6	8	5	1	4
2	1	8	7	4	9	3	6	5
7	5	3	6	1	2	4	8	9
6	4	9	8	3	5	1	2	7
4	7	5	9	2	1	6	3	8
8	9	1	3	5	6	7	4	2
3	2	6	4	8	7	9	5	1

Solutions

20

	V	S		F		L	
P	E	D	I	G	R	E	E
	N	A	G		E	N	I	D
	D	I	N	N	E	R		R
Y	E	S		E		I	C	Y
	T		K	W	A	C	H	A
A	T	L	A	S		H	A	D
	A		R		M		T	
		M	A	J	O	R		P
T	R	I	O		P	O	L	E
	I	N	K	Y		L	E	A
O	G	E	E		W	E	D	S

Answer: KINDLINESS

21

22

```
S U B J U G A T E   B   R   P
Y   A   R   U   O R D E A L   L
S U R C H A R G E   A   P   A
T   A   N   R E V E L R Y
E X T R U D I N G   E   I   M
M   A   E   O W L   C   A
  C O N Q U E S T   Y E A S T
S   D   R   A   H   M   E
T O P A Z   G Y R A T I N G
R   E   O V A   R   G   E
I   E   O   B O O M E R A N G
C A R A M E L   L   A   R
K   A   I   E F F E C T I V E
E N G I N E   R   S   E   S
N   E   G   C O N S I D E R S
```

23

24

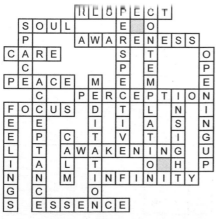

(RESPECT, SOUL, AWARENESS, CARE, PEACE, PERCEPTION, FOCUS, AWAKENING, INFINITY, ESSENCE)

25

```
          A
        A N T
      A N G L E
    N O T E P A D
  V I G I L A N C E
P R A C T I C A B L E
I N S T I N C T I V E L Y
```

26

MILD - mile - mole - more - sore - sort - SOFT
(Other solutions are possible)

Solutions

27

28

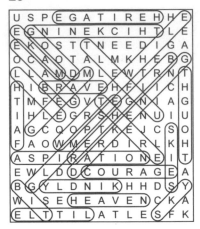

29

		H		D		C		
B	O	T	A	N	I	C	A	L
	L	O	U		E	N		
	D	E	L	E	T	I	O	N
B	A	D		R		S	E	A
	G		C	A	P	S		K
B	E	L	L			U	S	E
		A	G	R	E	E	D	
S	C	O	P	E			N	
	L		P	L	A	C	I	D
C	A	R	E		C	O	L	A
	N		D	O	T	T	E	D

Answer: ACCEPTANCE

30

6	5	3	2	7	8	9	4	1
9	7	2	1	4	6	3	5	8
8	4	1	9	5	3	6	7	2
4	9	5	6	1	2	7	8	3
1	3	6	8	9	7	4	2	5
7	2	8	5	3	4	1	9	6
5	6	7	3	8	9	2	1	4
2	1	9	4	6	5	8	3	7
3	8	4	7	2	1	5	6	9

31

Z		R		E	X	H	A	U	S	T	I	B	L	E
E	J	E	C	T		E		U		M		I		
S		C		H	A	N	D	I	C	A	P	P	E	D
T	I	T	L	E		C		H		L		G		
F		A		R		E	M	P	L	O	Y	E	E	S
U		N	E	E	D		O		I		V			P
L	A	G		A		N		K		P	A	I	R	
N		U		L	A	S	S	O	E	D		P		E
E	E	L	S		P		T		O		O	V	A	
S		A		P		E		Y	O	U	R		D	
S	C	R	A	W	L	E	R	S		R		A		S
	H		S		I		O		B	O	T	C	H	
C	O	N	S	E	Q	U	E	N	C	E		I		E
	K		E		U		I		L	O	O	S	E	
A	E	S	T	H	E	T	I	C	A	L		N		T

32

F

Solutions

33

34

35

36

37

	B		R	A	M	
	L	A	V	A		A	L	P
	O	P	I	N	E	D		R
O	B	O	E			E	M	U
		S	W	A	G	M	A	N
		T		P		O	N	E
B	U	L	L	E	T	I	N	
	S	E	E	R		S	A	C
	U		G	I	B	E		A
G	R	E	A	T		L	S	D
	E		T	I	L	L	E	R
B	R	I	E	F		E	W	E

Answer: PATIENCE

38

5	7	6	9	3	2	8	4	1
3	9	1	4	6	8	7	5	2
2	4	8	7	1	5	3	6	9
9	6	4	2	7	3	1	8	5
7	1	5	6	8	4	9	2	3
8	3	2	5	9	1	6	7	4
6	5	9	3	4	7	2	1	8
1	2	3	8	5	6	4	9	7
4	8	7	1	2	9	5	3	6

Solutions

39

40

41

42

Answer: MEDITATION

43

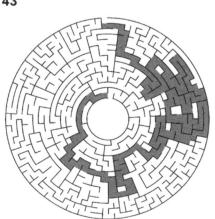

44

E
A rooftop is missing to the left of the tallest tower.

Solutions

45

```
 |J| | |T| |P| | 
M|O|N|G|R|E|L| |S
 |E| | |U|S|U|R|P
D|Y|S|P|E|P|S|I|A
 | |U| | |Y| |C
D|U|M|P|S| |L|E|G
 |S| |A|U|R|A| |O
C|H|O|R|E| |G|A|D
 |E| |A| |S| |N
C|R|A|B| |T|O|G|A
 | |S|L|E|E|V|E|S
A|P|S|E| |T|A|L|K
```

Answer: CONSCIOUS

46

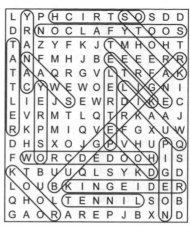

```
L Y P H C I R T S O S D D
D R N O C L A F Y T O O S
T A Z Y F K J T M H O H T
A N F M H J B E E E E R R
A A Q R G V L T R F A K
T C Y W E W O E L I G N I
L I E J S E W R D I K E C
E V R M T L Q T R K A A J
R K P M I Q V E F G X U W
D H S X O J G P V H U P Q
F W O R C D E D O O H I S
K T B U U Q L S Y K D G D
L O U B K I N G E I D E R
Q H O L T E N N I L S O B
G A O R A R E P J B X N D
```

47

```
S U P E R ■ M A J O R E T T E
E ■ Y ■ I ■ A ■ A ■ E ■ ■ R
B U L L D O Z E R ■ V I S T A
A ■ O ■ D ■ E ■ D ■ E ■ L ■ S
C A N V A S ■ F I X A T I V E
E ■ ■ ■ N ■ S ■ N ■ L ■ C ■
O P T I C ■ Q U I P ■ D I S C
U ■ W ■ E ■ U ■ E ■ B ■ N ■ A
S K I D ■ H A I R ■ O U G H T
■ ■ T ■ F ■ B ■ E ■ T ■ ■ A
S U C C U M B S ■ P A R S E C
I ■ H ■ N ■ L ■ W ■ N ■ T ■ L
D O Y E N ■ I M A G I N A R Y
E ■ ■ ■ E ■ N ■ F ■ S ■ I ■ S
S P O T L I G H T ■ T H R U M
```

48

1	9	4	8	7	3	5	2	6
5	7	6	1	4	2	3	8	9
8	2	3	5	6	9	7	1	4
6	5	1	3	2	4	9	7	8
7	3	8	6	9	1	4	5	2
2	4	9	7	5	8	1	6	3
4	8	5	2	3	7	6	9	1
3	1	7	9	8	6	2	4	5
9	6	2	4	1	5	8	3	7

49

```
 |I|L|V|E|R|F|E|W| |L|I|M|E
W| |A| | |A| | |U| | | |S
Y| |R| |G|Y|P|S|O|P|H|I|L|A
C| |W| |W| |P| |I| |N| |X
H| |I| |C|O|R|M| |N| |C| |I
E| |G| |R| |P| | |I| |F
L| | | |T|A|R|R|A|G|O|N| |R
M|O|W|E|R| |U| |O| |R| |A
 |H| | |B| |P| |A| |R| |G
 |W|I|S|T|E|R|I|A| |P|L|A|N|E
S| |T| |U| |E| |G| |E| |T
T| |E| |R| |T|O|A|D|S|T|O|O|L
O| |F| |N| |I| |T| | |R| |A
C|U|L|T|I|V|A|T|O|R| | | |W
K| |Y| |P| | |R| |A|S|P|E|N
```

50

A and J,
B and G,
C and H,
D and I,
E and L,
F and K.

Solutions

51

52

53

	M		S			T		J
F	O	R	T	U	N	A	T	E
	I		O			T		S
B	R	O	A	D	C	A	S	T
	E	X	T	O	L		K	
		E		S	U	M	U	P
B	I	N			B	A	L	I
	N		N			E	L	M
B	E	S	I	D	E	S		E
	R	A	T	E		T	I	N
E	T	C		B	U	R	N	T
		K	I	T		O	N	O

Answer: FOCUS

54

9	2	4	3	1	5	7	6	8
6	1	8	9	7	2	5	4	3
3	5	7	8	4	6	2	9	1
5	3	1	6	2	9	4	8	7
2	7	6	4	8	3	9	1	5
8	4	9	1	5	7	3	2	6
1	8	2	7	3	4	6	5	9
4	9	3	5	6	1	8	7	2
7	6	5	2	9	8	1	3	4

55

56

Solutions

57

58

59

60

```
              B
            P E R
          D E L T A
        E M P O W E R
      M O T I V A T E D
    C A N D L E L I G H T
  P E R P E N D I C U L A R
```

61

The nine-letter words are:
MASTERING and STREAMING

62

Answer: SERENITY

63

8	6	7	1	5	9	2	3	4
9	4	3	2	8	6	5	1	7
2	5	1	3	4	7	9	8	6
3	2	9	4	7	1	8	6	5
7	1	5	6	2	8	4	9	3
4	8	6	9	3	5	1	7	2
6	7	4	8	9	2	3	5	1
1	3	8	5	6	4	7	2	9
5	9	2	7	1	3	6	4	8

Solutions

64

65

66

67

Answer: AWARENESS

68

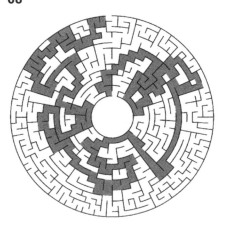

69

H	A	B	I	T	A	T
D	E	V	O	T	E	D
A	N	E	M	O	N	E
C	A	N	D	L	E	S
G	I	R	A	F	F	E
T	A	C	T	F	U	L
J	O	U	R	N	A	L

Solutions

70

	P	A		N		W
P	R	A	C	T	I	C	E
	O	U	R		N	U	T	S
	C	L	E	V	E	R		U
O	L	D		E		V	A	N
	A		S	A	T	E	E	N
L	I	B	E	L		D	R	Y
	M		C		A		Y
		F	L	I	R	T		Y
P	E	R	U		T	O	D	O
	L	A	D	Y		L	O	G
S	K	Y	E		U	L	N	A

Answer: ATTENTION

71

72

73

3	6	1	9	5	8	2	4	7
2	7	9	6	4	3	1	8	5
8	5	4	1	7	2	3	6	9
5	2	8	7	1	6	4	9	3
4	3	6	2	9	5	8	7	1
1	9	7	3	8	4	5	2	6
6	4	2	5	3	9	7	1	8
9	1	5	8	2	7	6	3	4
7	8	3	4	6	1	9	5	2

74

75

76

COIN - corn - core - care - cane -
cant - CENT
(Other solutions are possible)

Solutions

77

78

79

	S			G			I	
	H	A	B	I	T	A	T	
	O	P	A	L		A	C	T
	W	R	I	T		R	H	O
K	N	I	T			O		M
		C		H	I	N	G	E
	P	O	W	E	R		E	
H	A	T		A	O	R	T	A
	U			D	N	A		L
	S	T	E	W		T	W	O
L	E	O		A	D	I	E	U
		T	O	Y		O	D	D

Answer: INSPIRATION

80

4	5	6	2	7	8	1	3	9
7	8	3	4	1	9	6	5	2
1	9	2	5	6	3	8	4	7
6	4	8	3	2	5	9	7	1
5	7	9	1	4	6	2	8	3
3	2	1	8	9	7	5	6	4
8	3	4	9	5	1	7	2	6
9	6	5	7	3	2	4	1	8
2	1	7	6	8	4	3	9	5

81

C	R	A	Y	O	N		P	R	O	J	E	C	T	S
R		V		R		I		O		H			M	
E	X	E	R	C	I	S	E	S		I	M	A	G	E
E		R		H		O		L		N		N		L
P	L	A	T	E	A	U		E	X	T	I	N	C	T
		G		S		T		E			E			
W	H	E	A	T		H	O	P	E	F	U	L	L	Y
A			R			W		R			R			E
S	U	B	M	A	R	I	N	E		E	X	I	S	T
		L		D		R		Q		N				
S	E	A	S	I	D	E		R	O	U	T	I	N	E
T		Z		N		A		O		E			T	
A	L	I	E	N		S	H	R	I	N	K	I	N	G
I		N		E			A			C			A	
R	E	G	A	R	D	E	D		C	Y	C	L	E	D

82

4

Solutions

83

84

85

86
E

87

					14			人		
E	D	D	A		S	T	I	R		
	R	E	T	C	H	E	D			
	E	V	E		O	M	A	N		
T	W	O	S	T	E	P		A		
	U			S	O	A	P			
P	A	R	C	H			W			
	M		L	A	T	E	N	T		
D	O	N	O	R		Q		R		
	E		S	E	C	U	R	E		
A	B	L	E		R	A	Y	S		
	A		S	T	Y	L	E	S		

Answer: BREATHING

88

8	5	7	3	1	2	4	6	9
6	4	1	9	5	8	2	3	7
3	9	2	4	7	6	5	1	8
4	2	9	7	3	1	6	8	5
5	3	6	8	2	4	7	9	1
7	1	8	5	6	9	3	2	4
1	8	3	6	4	5	9	7	2
9	7	4	2	8	3	1	5	6
2	6	5	1	9	7	8	4	3

Solutions

89

90

91

92

Answer: WAKEFULNESS

93

94

Solutions

95

	S		T			O		
	P	A	R	I	A	H		V
H	Y	D	E		R	I	P	E
		H	A	N	G	O	U	T
A	B	E	D		U		E	
		R		R	E	T	R	O
	M	E	R	E	D	I	T	H
	E			C		T	O	M
C	A	R	P	E	T		R	
	L	A	U	D		W	I	N
		C	R	E	V	I	C	E
F	I	E	L	D		T	O	W

Answer: MANTRA

96

97

98

5	2	4	6	7	8	3	1	9
3	8	1	5	9	4	2	7	6
6	9	7	3	1	2	8	4	5
4	3	8	7	6	5	9	2	1
2	6	5	1	4	9	7	8	3
7	1	9	8	2	3	6	5	4
8	5	6	2	3	1	4	9	7
1	4	3	9	8	7	5	6	2
9	7	2	4	5	6	1	3	8

99

(crossword grid)

100

The chocolate stick in the top is shorter.

Solutions

101

102

103

	B		C			D		B
C	A	V	A	L	C	A	D	E
	S		M			T		A
F	I	R	E	A	L	A	R	M
	N	A	O	M	I		O	
		S		P	A	N	T	S
A	S	H			R	I	O	T
	P		W			B	R	A
W	A	S	H	T	U	B		T
	S	T	Y	E		L	I	E
E	M	U		S	M	E	L	L
		N	O	T		S	L	Y

Answer: PURPOSE

104

7	4	9	6	3	8	2	1	5
2	6	8	9	1	5	3	7	4
1	3	5	2	7	4	9	6	8
6	5	7	8	4	3	1	2	9
9	1	4	5	2	7	6	8	3
8	2	3	1	9	6	4	5	7
5	7	2	3	6	9	8	4	1
4	9	1	7	8	2	5	3	6
3	8	6	4	5	1	7	9	2

105

106

107

The nine-letter word is:
FASCINATE

Solutions

108

109

110

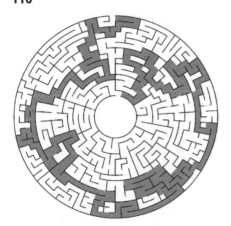

111

A and I,
B and J,
C and L,
D and K,
E and H,
F and G.

112

		п			L		
C	O	C	O		D	A	I	S
	P	A	S	T	I	M	E	
	A	S	S		S	I	D	E
C	L	I	E	N	T	S		N
	N			U	S	E	D	
D	O	O	R		R		K	
	C		E	M	B	L	E	M
A	L	A	M	O		I		A
	O		A	W	A	K	E	N
S	C	A	R		P	E	E	L
	K		K	E	E	N	L	Y

Answer: WISDOM

113

4	3	9	5	8	7	1	6	2
5	1	7	6	9	2	4	3	8
2	8	6	1	4	3	5	7	9
7	4	3	8	6	9	2	5	1
8	9	1	3	2	5	6	4	7
6	5	2	4	7	1	9	8	3
9	7	4	2	3	6	8	1	5
3	6	5	9	1	8	7	2	4
1	2	8	7	5	4	3	9	6

Solutions

114

B	A	N	G	L	E		P	R	E	S	U	M	E	S
E			L		R		O		K		E			W
A	D	J	U	T	A	N	T		S	I	Z	Z	L	E
R			T		S		A	X	E		Z			E
D	E	F	T		E	A	T		R	E	C	A	N	T
	L		O		R		O	F	F		N		M	
A	M	O	N	G	S	T		A	S	T	R	I	D	E
Q		P		N		I	N	K		I		N		A
U	N	E	Q	U	A	L		E	S	C	H	E	A	T
A		R		L	E	T		H		I		G		T
P	E	A	N	U	T		H	O	E		R	H	E	A
L		T		A	Y	E		A		S			A	U
A	T	O	N	E	R		O	B	T	R	U	D	E	D
N		R		V		R			R		H		T	I
E	A	S	T	E	R	L	Y		E	X	E	M	P	T

115

116

117

Answer: RESOLUTION

118

119

120

TIME - tile - wile - wild - weld -
weed - WEEK
(Other solutions are possible)

Solutions

121

	I		H		S		
M	E	D	I	C	A	L	
	A	X	I	S		B	A	D
	G	A	G	S		A	G	E
H	O	L	S			S		A
		T		A	M	E	N	D
	H	E	N	N	A		O	
B	U	D		A	L	E	R	T
	M			L	I	P		O
	U	G	L	Y		O	A	T
U	S	E		S	U	C	R	E
		M	O	T		H	E	M

Answer: COMPASSION

122

123

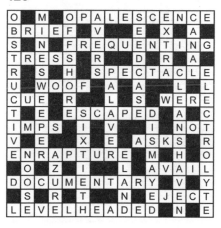

124

3	9	6	8	5	7	4	1	2
4	2	8	1	3	9	5	7	6
1	5	7	2	4	6	3	9	8
8	1	4	3	6	2	9	5	7
2	7	3	9	1	5	6	8	4
9	6	5	4	7	8	2	3	1
7	3	9	6	8	4	1	2	5
6	8	2	5	9	1	7	4	3
5	4	1	7	2	3	8	6	9

125

126

I	M	A	G	I	N	E
O	N	E	S	E	L	F
W	I	S	T	F	U	L
H	O	R	I	Z	O	N
S	N	U	G	G	L	E
T	H	O	U	G	H	T
C	O	M	F	O	R	T

Solutions

127

128

129

	T		L		P		P	
	H	O	O	L	I	G	A	N
	A	R	C		C		P	
N	I	G	H	T	C	L	U	B
		A		H	A	L	A	L
	A	N	G	O	L	A		E
	W			R	I	N	S	E
K	E	P	T		L	O	U	D
		A			L		D	
U	R	S	A	M	I	N	O	R
	O	S	L	O		A	K	A
	Y	E	L	P		G	U	T

Answer: COURAGE

130

4	7	6	9	5	3	2	8	1
5	8	3	4	1	2	6	9	7
9	2	1	7	6	8	4	3	5
7	6	4	1	9	5	3	2	8
2	5	9	3	8	4	1	7	6
3	1	8	2	7	6	5	4	9
1	4	5	8	2	7	9	6	3
6	3	7	5	4	9	8	1	2
8	9	2	6	3	1	7	5	4

131

132

Solutions

133

134

135

136

137

The nine-letter word is:
SOMETHING

138

Answer: STILLNESS

139

6	8	4	3	2	7	9	5	1
3	7	1	4	9	5	8	6	2
2	9	5	8	1	6	7	4	3
8	2	6	1	4	9	5	3	7
7	4	3	2	5	8	1	9	6
5	1	9	7	6	3	4	2	8
4	3	8	9	7	2	6	1	5
1	5	2	6	8	4	3	7	9
9	6	7	5	3	1	2	8	4

Solutions

140

141

142

143

Answer: LEARNING

144

145

8	1	2	4	9	7	3	6	5
4	5	9	2	3	6	8	1	7
7	6	3	1	5	8	4	9	2
1	4	7	5	8	9	2	3	6
3	8	5	7	6	2	9	4	1
2	9	6	3	4	1	5	7	8
9	2	8	6	7	4	1	5	3
5	7	4	8	1	3	6	2	9
6	3	1	9	2	5	7	8	4

Solutions

146

	L		S			V		
	Y	I	P	P	E	E		S
M	E	M	O		S	E	C	T
	P	O	R	T	R	A	Y	
A	K	I	N		A		N	
	S		S	T	A	N	D	
W	H	I	T	E	S	E	A	
E			E		P	L	Y	
F	E	N	D	E	R		L	
	P	E	E	P		M	O	A
	R	E	L	I	A	N	T	
M	O	O	D	Y		D	I	M

Answer: MOTIVATION

147

148

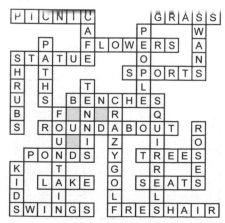

F	A	S	C	I	N	A	T	E		W	A	S	T	E
E		U		R		S		B		H		Q		T
A	M	B	E	R		T	A	B	L	E	A	U		H
S		J		U		E		S		N		A		I
T	R	U	M	P	E	R	Y		H	E	C	T	I	C
		D		T			D		V					A
S	W	I	G		M	A	N	A	G	E	R	I	A	L
N		C		G		V		Z		R		N		L
O	V	E	R	L	O	O	K	E	D		S	E	X	Y
W				E		W			F		L			
F	O	R	M	A	L		A	S	P	I	R	A	N	T
L		A		M		S		E		N		S		H
A		B	L	I	N	K	E	R		I	N	T	E	R
K		B		N		I		V		S		I		E
E	K	I	N	G		T	O	O	T	H	A	C	H	E

149

D

On all of the other balls the black segments are diametrically opposite white segments.

150

P	I	C	N	I	C			G	R	A	S	S
			A			P				W	
		P		F	L	O	W	E	R	S	A	
S	T	A	T	U	E		O			A	N	
H		T			S	P	O	R	T	S	
R		H		T		L					
U		S		B	E	N	C	H	E	S	
B			F		N		R		Q		
S		R	O	U	N	D	A	B	O	U	T	R
			U		I		Z		I		O	
	P	O	N	D	S		Y		T	R	E	E	S
K			T		G			R		E	
I		L	A	K	E		S	E	A	T	S	
D			I		O			L			
S	W	I	N	G	S		F	R	E	S	H	A	I	R

151

A

Solutions

152

153

154

	A		U		I		P	
	P	A	R	A	N	O	I	D
	S	U	N		H		L	
R	E	D		T	A	L	O	N
		I		A	B	A	T	E
	S	T	U	P	I	D		E
	O			S	T	E	E	D
A	N	T	I		I	N	N	S
		A			N		D	
A	M	B	E	R	G	R	I	S
	A	L	T	O		A	V	E
	P	E	A	T		P	E	A

Answer: LOVING

155

3	1	7	5	8	2	9	6	4
8	4	5	9	6	7	1	2	3
2	9	6	4	1	3	7	5	8
6	3	8	7	9	4	2	1	5
7	2	9	3	5	1	4	8	6
1	5	4	6	2	8	3	7	9
9	8	1	2	3	6	5	4	7
4	6	3	1	7	5	8	9	2
5	7	2	8	4	9	6	3	1

156

A	K	I	M	B	O		V		F		W	A	F	T
S		M		O		Z	E	N	I	T	H			A
S	M	A	L	L	P	O	X		V		E	M	I	R
E		G		U		N		J	E	S	T			T
T	R	O	U	S	S	E	A	U			S	O	F	A
	E			P			D	U	C	T				R
B	A	C	K	G	A	M	M	O	N		O	N	C	E
	C		N		R		O		I		N			H
S	H	O	O		S	U	B	A	Q	U	E	O	U	S
Y			W	E	E	P		U			R			
R	E	E	L			O	B	S	E	R	V	A	N	T
I			E	A	R	N		E		I		B		A
N	E	E	D		A		D	A	I	N	T	I	E	R
G			G	A	R	T	E	R		D		D		O
E	P	E	E		E		N		A	S	P	E	C	T

157

158

CITY - pity - pits - pots - tots - tows - TOWN
(Other solutions are possible)

Solutions

159

L	U	K	E	W	A	R	M					C	
			A		P	A	S	S	I	O	N		
		B		A	D					V		E	
P	A	R	A	F	F	I	N					V	E
S		L	M		A	T	S	U	M	M	E	R	Y
U		M	Y		K	E	R	O	S	E	N	E	H
L	T	F		V		I	C			E	A		
T	E	M	P	E	R	A	T	E	D	N	T	T	
R		V		E	R	R	I						
Y	T	E	P	I	D		R	D	R	I			
C		R		D	I	C							
O	F	I	R	E	G	L	O	W	I	N	G		
A		S		A	W	T							
F	L	U	S	H	E	D	S	U	N	N	Y		

160

161

162

A   B   C   D   E   F

163

		K			H		
I	R	O	N		S	L	O	T
	O	P	I	N	I	O	N
	B	E	T		G	O	E	S
P	E	R	S	O	N	S		A
	A			S	E	N	D
A	I	S	L	E			E
	S		A	R	R	O	W	S
C	O	A	T	I		L		H
	B		E	E	R	I	L	Y
P	A	S	S		O	V	A	L
	R		T	W	E	E	D	Y

Answer: HAPPINESS

164

1	7	9	3	4	2	5	8	6
4	5	8	7	6	1	2	9	3
3	2	6	9	5	8	7	1	4
7	4	1	6	9	5	8	3	2
2	9	3	4	8	7	6	5	1
8	6	5	2	1	3	9	4	7
6	8	4	1	7	9	3	2	5
9	3	7	5	2	4	1	6	8
5	1	2	8	3	6	4	7	9

Solutions

165

S	I	F	T	S		P	A	R	O	D	Y	I	N	G
T		L		K		L		E		E				O
A	N	O	N	Y	M	O	U	S		C	O	R	G	I
R		W		L		Y		I		A		U		N
B	A	N	D	I	T		B	L	I	N	K	I	N	G
O			G		W		I		T		N			
A	W	A	S	H		A	M	E	N		H	O	L	D
R		E		T		L		N		C		U		E
D	I	R	T		B	L	O	C		O	A	S	I	S
		O		F		F		E		Q				C
D	I	S	C	I	P	L	E		J	U	G	G	L	E
I		O		E		O		M		E		R		N
V	O	L	T	S		W	R	I	S	T	B	A	N	D
O			T			E		N		R		Z		E
T	E	S	T	A	T	R	I	X		Y	I	E	L	D

166

167

H	A	W	T	H	O	R	N				
A			A					B	A	N	A	N	A
Z			X		L					C		S
E		T	U	L	I	P		O	S	I	E	R		P
L			S		M				Y		R		I
	T			H	E	M	L	O	C	K		N
	H				A			A		P		D
	U		W	Y	C	H	E	L	M		E		L
	J		I		O			O	R	A	N	G	E
B	A	L	S	A		G		R		R		I
I		T		A	S	P	E	N		I	N
R		L	E	M	O	N			B		K
C		R			Y	E	W		M	A	N	G	O
H		I						L		O
	B	R	A	Z	I	L		P	L	U	M

168

7